Gerd Klawitter

# Zeitzeichensender

## Time Signal Stations

Siebel Verlag

CIP-Titelaufnahme der Deutschen Bibliothek:

**Klawitter, Gerd:**
Zeitzeichensender = Time signal stations / Gerd Klawitter. – 11.
Aufl. – Meckenheim : Siebel, 1988
   Bis 10. Aufl. im Scheunemann-Verl., Köln
   ISBN 3-922221-29-7

Wir danken der Fa. Rohde & Schwarz,
München, für die freundliche Überlassung
des Titelfotos

Cover photo by the courtesy of the
Rohde & Schwarz Co., Munich, FRG

ISBN 3-922221-29-7
11. Auflage 1988

Herstellung: betz-druck gmbh, Darmstadt-Arheilgen

# Vorwort

Seit dem Erscheinen der 10. Ausgabe dieses Buches im Jahre 1983 haben sich derart zahlreiche Änderungen bei den Zeitzeichensendern ergeben, daß eine völlige Neubearbeitung des Buches erforderlich geworden ist.
Ergänzt wurde die vorliegende Ausgabe darüber hinaus um drei weitere Kapitel:
— Erläutert werden eingehend der Aufbau und die Wirkungsweise von Atomfrequenznormalen, dem Herz aller Zeitzeichensender.
— Kein Atomfrequenznormal ist *das* absolut korrekte Normal, sondern es werden weltweit ständig Zeiten und Frequenzen eingesetzter Atomfrequenznormale mit einem aufwendigen Verfahren verglichen und gemittelt.
— Immer mehr Zeitzeichensender übertragen seit ein paar Jahren die Zeit zusätzlich in codierter Form zur Fernsteuerung von Funkuhren. In einem besonderen Kapitel werden einige derartige im Handel erhältliche Uhren vorgestellt.

Den folgenden Firmen und Instituten danke ich für die freundliche Überlassung von Foto- und Skizzenmaterial, das die verbale Erläuterung technischer Details erheblich erleichtert hat:
Ball Efratom Division, Irvine, Cal., USA
Bureau Internationale de l'Heure, Paris
Hewlett Packard GmbH, Böblingen
OSA Oscilloquartz SA, Neuchâtel, Schweiz
Rohde & Schwarz, München
Unverdross-Technik, München

Mein besonderer Dank gilt Herrn Rainer Unverdross für die fachtechnische Prüfung des Manuskripts.

Coesfeld, im Januar 1988

Gerd Klawitter

# Preface

Since the appearance of this book's 10th edition in 1983, a lot of changes have occurred on the Time Signal Stations' schedules. As a consequence, a completely revised new edition became necessary now.
In addition the following three chapters were added to the book:
— Explanations on the concept of Atomic Frequency Standards, the heart of each Time Signal Station.
— None of the Atomic Frequency Standards is *the* absolutely correct standard. Times and frequencies of all worldwide existing Atomic Frequency Standards are continuously compared and adjusted.
— A few years ago, more and more Time Signal Stations started the emission of coded time signals for wireless remote control purposes of electronic clocks. In a special chapter of this book some of such clocks available to everyone are presented.

I thank the following firms and institutes for kindly supplying us with photos and pictures, which made the verbal explanation of technical details much easier:
Ball Efratom Division, Irvine, Cal., USA
Bureau Internationale de l'Heure, Paris
Hewlett Packard, Böblingen, FRG
OSA Oscilloquartz SA, Neuchâtel, Switzerland
Rohde & Schwarz, Munich
Unverdross-Technik, Munich

My special thanks go to Mr. Rainer Unverdross for the final technical checkup of the book's manuscript.

Coesfeld, January 1988

Gerd Klawitter

# Inhalt

# Content

| Inhalt | Seite/Page | Content |
|---|---|---|

## 2. Zeit und Frequenz

Die Zeit (T) und die Frequenz (f) sind zwei voneinander untrennbar verbundene Begriffe:

$$f = \frac{1}{T}.$$

Unter dem Begriff „Frequenz" (f) versteht man die Anzahl von Ereignissen innerhalb eines bestimmten „Zeitraumes" (T).

Eine „Uhrzeit" ist

$$= \frac{\text{Gesamtsumme von Ereignissen}}{\text{Zahl der Ereignisse pro Zeiteinheit}}$$

Eine „Uhr" besteht somit aus
1) einem Frequenzstandard und
2) einem Zählwerk, mit dem irgendwelche Ereignisse gezählt werden.

Dieses Zählwerk war ursprünglich — bevor der Mensch mechanische Uhren erfand — die Erdrotation. Später nutzte man mechanische Pendel, dann Quarzoszillatoren und heute Atomfrequenznormale.

Wird in diesem Buch einmal von der Frequenz und einmal von der Zeit gesprochen, so ist das beabsichtigt und zulässig.

## 2. Time and Frequency

The "time" (T) and the "frequency" (f) are two synonyms which can not be separated from each other:

$$f = \frac{1}{T}.$$

The synonym "frequency" (f) stands for a number of events that occur within a fixed "time" (T).

The "clock time" can be defined as

$$\frac{\text{total number of events}}{\text{number of events per unit of time}}.$$

A "clock" is
1) a frequency standard and
2) a mechanism counting any events.

This "counting mechanism" once — before man invented the mechanical clock — has been the earth's rotation. Later man used a mechanical pendulum, then quartz crystal oscillators and today we are using atomic frequency standards.

So if we mention the two words "time" and "frequency" within this book, please remember that each of these two words stands for the other one, too.

# 3. Zeiteinheiten

## 3.1. Ephemeridensekunde (1956-1967)

1956 definierte das Internationale Komitee für Maß und Gewicht die Sekunde als Grundeinheit der Zeit mit einer Größenordnung von einem 31 556 925.9747ten Teil des tropischen Jahres. Das tropische Jahr ist die Zeitdauer zwischen zwei aufeinanderfolgenden Durchgängen der ,,mittleren Sonne" durch den ,,mittleren Frühlingspunkt". Als Definition wurde das differentielle tropische Jahr zum Zeitpunkt 31. Dezember 1899 12 Uhr Weltzeit festgelegt. Das tropische Jahr bestand aus 365 Tagen, 5 Stunden, 48 Minuten und 46 Sekunden zu jener Zeit und nimmt seither um etwa 5.3 ms pro Jahr ab.

Die Epheremeridensekunde kann somit nur sehr ungenau ermittelt werden. Obwohl diese Zeiteinheit sehr präzise definiert ist, kann sie von astronomischen Observatorien nur in Teilen von $10^{-9}$ bestimmt werden. In der Praxis wird die Ephemeridensekunde mit Hilfe der Mondposition ermittelt. Der Umlauf des Mondes wurde mittels langfristiger Vergleiche mit dem Erdumlauf als ,,kalibriertes sekundäres Normal" angesehen.

## 3.2. Cäsiumstrahl-Zeitnormale (seit 1967)

Die Hyperfeinstruktur-Übergangsfrequenz im Grundzustand des Cäsiumatoms ermöglicht eine sehr viel genauere und einheitlichere Zeitmessung, und zwar mit einer Ungenauigkeit kleiner als $5 \times 10^{-12}$. Das Frequenznormal der Station WWV beispielsweise hat eine Ungenauigkeit von weniger als $1 \times 10^{-12}$, das der PTB Braunschweig sogar von weniger als $0.65 \times 10^{-14}$. Die Sekunde wurde von der 12. General-

# 3. Time Scales

## 3.1. Ephemeris Time

The International Committee of Weights and Measures in 1956 defined the fundamental unit of time, the second, as $1/31 556 925.9747$ of the tropical year. The tropical year is the interval between two consecutive returns of the sun to the vernal equinox. The tropical year was defined for December 31, 1899 12h ephemeris time. It consisted of 365 days, 5 hours, 48 minutes and 46 seconds at that time and has been decreasing by about 5.3 ms per year since that time.

Ephemeris time has not been defined very exactly. It can only be measured by astronomical observatories in parts of $10^{-9}$. In practice, ephemeris time is determined by observations of the moon.

## 3.2. Atomic Time

The zero-field transition of the cesium-atom makes possible a much more precise and standard measurement of time with an uncertainty less than $5 \times 10^{-12}$. The uncertainty of station WWV, for instance, is less than $1 \times 10^{-12}$, that of the PTB Braunschweig, FRG, is less than $0.65 \times 10^{-14}$. The zero-field transition for cesium has been measured in terms of the ephemeris second to be

konferenz für Maß und Gewicht im Jahre 1964 folgendermaßen definiert: „Die Sekunde ist das 9 192 631 770fache der Periodendauer der dem Übergang zwischen den beiden Hyperfeinstrukturenniveaus des Grundzustandes von Atomen des Nuklids $^{133}$Cs entsprechenden Strahlung." Andere Definitionen können zu gegebener Zeit beschlossen werden, falls noch exaktere Meßmethoden zur Verfügung stehen. So wurden zur Zeitmessung bereits Ammoniakstrahlmaser und der Wasserstoffmaser auf ihre Eignung als primäres Zeit- und Frequenznormal hin untersucht. Letzterer mit einer Periodendauer des 1 420 405 751.73fachen Überganges.

9 192 631 770 hertz. This standard was adopted at the 12th General Conference of Weights and Measures in 1964. Occasionally other standards may be adopted if more precise measurements are available. So, for instance, ammonium- and hydrogenmaser were tested, the latter with 1 420 405 751.73 hertz on this time scale.

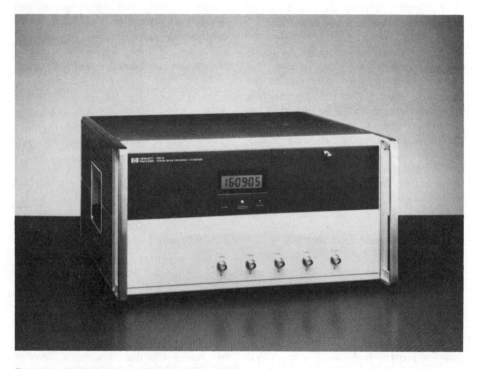

Ein Cäsiumstrahl-Normal (Hewlett-Packard)
A Cesium Beam Standard (Hewlett-Packard)

## 3.3. Erdrotationszeit

Diese Zeiteinheit basiert auf der mittleren Erdrotationsdauer. Sie wird durch Beobachtung von bestimmten Sternen bestimmt, sobald sie gewisse Meridiane überqueren. Die Erde rotiert einmal um 360 Grad in 23 Stunden, 56 Minuten und 4.09 Sekunden. Durch Schwankungen in der Rotation durch Gezeitenkopplung mit dem Mond (relativ um mehrere $10^{-8}$) sowie durch unvorhersehbare unsystematische Rotationsschwankungen (ebenfalls relativ um mehrere $10^{-8}$), die auf Massenverlagerungen im Erdinnern zurückzuführen sind, ist die Erdrotationszeit als Zeitnormal nicht genügend geeignet.

## 3.3. Sidereal Time

Sidereal time is based on the mean time of the earth's rotation. It is determined by observing certain stars when passing certain meridians. The mean sidereal day is 23 hours, 56 minutes and 4.09 seconds. Because of variations caused in oceal tides (relative greater than $10^{-8}$) and moving masses in the earth's center (also relative greater than $10^{-8}$), sidereal time is not perfectly uniform.

## 3.4. Weltzeit UT (Universal Time)

Die Weltzeit UT (vielfach auch Greenwich Mean Time genannt) ist die auf den Nullmeridian (Greenwich) bezogene mittlere Sonnenzeit. Da sich die Weltzeit im Verlauf des Jahres ständig ändert, wurde der Tag auf exakt 24 Stunden Dauer definiert. Der mittlere Sonnentag (von einem Sonnenhöchststand zum nächstfolgenden) hat wegen der Schiefe der Ekliptik (Erdbahn) und der Ellipsenform eine ziemlich unregelmäßige Länge. Von Astronomischen Observatorien gemessen wird er mit **UTØ** bezeichnet.

Im Jahresverlauf ändert sich die Rotationsgeschwindigkeit der Erde. Die Ursache dürfte in jahreszeitbedingten Winden der Nord- und Südhalbkugel zu finden sein. Außerdem ändert sich die äußere Form der Erde durch sich etwa halbjährlich geringfügig ändernde Sonnenintensität. Ferner befinden sich die größten Landmassen auf der Nordhalbkugel der Erde. Das hat im Frühling zur Folge, daß größere Massen (= Blätter von Bäumen und Sträuchern) um einige Meter

## 3.4. Universal Time (UT)

Universal time, also often known as Greenwich Mean Time, is based on the mean angle of the earth's rotation about its axis in relation to the sun. It refers to the prime meridian which passes through Greenwich, England. Since the Universal Time varies throughout the year, a mean solar day is defined as 24 hours exactly. Due to the slanting ecliptic of the earth and other reasons the mean solar day has a rather irregular length. Measured by astronomical observations, this time is named **UTØ.**

Annual variations occur in the speed of the earth's rotation. The reason may be found in seasonal changes in the wind patterns of the Northern and Southern hemispheres. Furthermore the earth's shape changes slightly due to changing solar activities. And there is another effect which causes irregularities in the earth's rotation: most of the continents are located in the Northern hemisphere. In spring the Northern hemisphere considerable masses (= the leaves of

vom Erdmittelpunkt entfernt und im Herbst (mit dem herabfallenden Laub) wieder näher zum Erdmittelpunkt gelangen. Der sich ergebende Effekt ist bei der Pirouette eines jeden Eiskunstläufers deutlich zu beobachten. Alle diese Effekte haben insgesamt zur Folge, daß die Erde sich etwa um den 1. Juni eines jeden Jahres am langsamsten dreht (sie „geht etwa 0.48 sec nach"). Etwa am 1. Oktober dreht sie sich am schnellsten (ca. 0.48 sec vor). Die Zeiteinheit UT0, korrigiert um die jahreszeitlich bedingten Faktoren, wird als **UT1** bezeichnet.

Weitere Unregelmäßigkeiten in der Erdrotation kommen durch Turbulenzen im Erdmagnetfeld hinzu. Außerdem bremsen die Gezeiten der Weltmeere die Rotation etwa in einer Größenordnung von 1 ms pro Jahrhundert. Wo immer diese Effekte in der Welt gemessen werden, erfolgt eine entsprechende Meldung an das Internationale Zeitbüro in Paris, das alle Meßwerte sammelt und statistisch die Zeit **UT2** errechnet.

Für Navigationszwecke und Raumforschung müssen Zeitsignale die Unregelmäßigkeit der Erdrotation beinhalten. Die überwiegende Zahl aller Zeitzeichensender strahlt daher UT2-Signale aus oder zumindest Informationen über die jeweilige Genauigkeit der Erdrotation.

## 3.5. Normalzeiten

Normalzeiten basieren auf UT oder UT2. Die Welt ist in 24 Zonen unterteilt, jede bestehend aus dem Bereich zwischen 15 Längengraden, entsprechend einer Stunde. Der durch Greenwich verlaufende Längengrad ist Mittellinie der „Nullzone", die 7.5 Längengrade nach Osten und Westen beinhaltet. Ostwärts von Greenwich aus werden die Zonen fortlau-

trees and bushes) move a few meters away from the earth's center, and in autumn (with the falling leaves) large masses again move nearer to the earth's center. The resulting effect can be seen in the skater's pirouette. As a result of all these occurrences the earth rotates slowly each year (minus 0.48 seconds) around June 1st. Around October 1st each year the earth rotates much faster than usual (plus 0.48 seconds). UT0 corrected for these periodic variations is called **UT1**.

Further irregulations in the earth's rotation depend on variations in the magnetic field of the earth. Additionally the ocean tides slowly reduce the earth rotation by approx. 1 ms per century. Wherever in the world such effects are measured, a special report is addressed to the Bureau International de l'Heure in Paris which collects all these data to calculate the time **UT2**.

For navigation purposes and space scientists, time signals must take irregular earth rotations into account. Most of the time signal radio stations therefore transmit UT2 signals or at least inform the receiver about the earth's rotation.

## 3.5. Standard Times

Standard times are based on UT or UT2. The world is divided into 24 zones, each 15 degrees of longtitude, or 1 hour angle, apart. The meridian passing through Greenwich is the center of the zero zone. This zone extends 7.5° east and west. Proceeding eastward from zero zone the zones are numbered 1 to 12 with the prefix "plus". Proceeding westward from

fend mit 1 bis 12 bezeichnet und mit einem positiven Vorzeichen (+) versehen. Um dort die örtliche Normalzeit zu erhalten, muß der Zeit in Greenwich die Zonennummer addiert werden. Westwärts von Greenwich aus entsprechend mit negativem Vorzeichen (−). Die tatsächlichen Zeitzonen werden von den Regierungen der Länder bestimmt und weichen daher zum Teil erheblich von den theoretischen Zeitzonen ab. In manchen Ländern weicht die Lokalzeit bis zu 30 oder 60 Minuten von der theoretischen Lokalzeit ab.

zone zero the zones are also numbered 1 to 12 but with the prefix "minus." To obtain the local standard time, the prefix plus the zone's number has to be added to Greenwich Mean Time. The actual boundaries of time zones are defined by law or custom within the various countries and generally do not coincide with the theoretical time zones. In some countries the local standard times even differ by 30 or 60 minutes from the theoretical standard time.

## 3.6. Koordinierte Weltzeit (UTC)

UTC ist die vom Pariser Internationalen Zeitbüro behandelte Zeit. Sie ist die weltweit koordinierte Zeit, auf die alle Normalfrequenzen und Normalzeiten aufgebaut werden. Sie steht in einem exakten Verhältnis zur internationalen Atomzeit, wenngleich sie sich um mehrere Sekunden von ihr unterscheiden kann.

Die UTC-Zeitskala wird der UT1-Zeitskala durch Hinzufügen oder Weglassen von Sekunden (Positive oder Negative Schaltsekunden!) angenähert.

## 3.6. Coordinated Universal Time (UTC)

UTC is the time scale maintained by the Bureau International de l'Heure. It forms the basis of a coordinated dissemination of standard frequencies and standard time. It corresponds exactly in rate to the International Atomic Time, although it differs from that time by an integral number of seconds. The UTC scale is adjusted to UT1 scale by the insertion or deletion of seconds (positive or negative leap seconds).

## 3.7. Zeitkorrekturen (DUT1)

Seit dem 01.01.1972 wird die koordinierte Weltzeit (UTC) nicht mehr in periodischen Zeitabständen der UT1-Zeit angeglichen, sondern in wesentlich kürzeren Zeitabständen, so daß nie mehr als 1 Sekunde Abweichung pro Jahr auftreten kann. Korrekturen der UTC werden schrittweise in einer Größenordnung von jeweils genau einer Sekunde (der sog. „Schaltsekunde") nach Angaben des Internationalen Zeitbüros eingeflochten. Die Schaltsekunden bewirken, daß die UTC-

## 3.7. Time Corrections (DUT1)

Since January 1st, 1972 the new UTC rate is no longer adjusted to UT1 periodically but at considerably shorter intervals. Thus the difference between UTC and UT1 never become longer than 1 second per year. Corrections to UTC are made in step adjustments of exactly 1 second (socalled "leap-seconds") as directed by the Bureau International de l'Heure. The leap-second adjustments ensure that the broadcasted UTC-signals never differ from UT1 by more than ± 0.7 sec. The

Zeitsignale nunmehr maximal ± 0.7 Sekunden von UT1 (nicht mehr UT2) abweichen.

Die Schaltsekunden werden im Bedarfsfall am letzten Tag eines Monats eingeflochten, bevorzugt am 31. Dezember und 30. Juni, und zwar zwischen dem Ende der 60. Sekunde der letzten Minute des letzten Tags des Monats und dem Beginn der nächsten Minute. Die Minute, in der diese Korrektur durchgeführt wird, besitzt entweder 59 oder 61 Sekunden, je nachdem ob die Korrektur negativ oder positiv.

Falls eine noch genauere UTC-Zeitangabe als ± 0.7 Sekunden erforderlich ist, so kann die Differenz aus UT1-UTC bis auf 0.1 Sekunden Genauigkeit jederzeit in codierter Form zahlreichen Zeitzeichenaussendungen entnommen werden. Die Stationen WWV/WWVH beispielsweise senden bestimmte Sekundenimpulse doppelt: Eine doppelte Aussendung des 1. bis 7. Sekundenimpulses bedeutet eine „positive Korrektur"; eine doppelte Aussendung der 9. bis 15. Sekundenimpulse deutet auf eine „negative Korrektur". Der 8. Sekundenimpuls ist nicht codiert. Die Größenordnung der Korrektur – in 0,1 Sekundeneinheiten – kann bei den Stationen WWV und WWVH ermittelt werden, indem die Anzahl der doppelten Sekundenimpulse gezählt wird. Beispiel: Die 1., 2. und 3. Sekunde werden verdoppelt ausgestrahlt: Die UT1-Korrektur beträgt „plus 0.3 Sekunden". Oder: Die 9. bis einschließlich 14. Sekunde werden verdoppelt ausgestrahlt: Die UT1-Korrektur beträgt „minus 0.6 Sekunden". Um UT1 zu erhalten, sind die v. g. Werte der jeweiligen koordinierten Weltzeit (UTC) hinzuzufügen, falls „Plus" gesendet wird; sie ist abzuziehen, falls „Minus" gesendet wird. Eine durch UTC-Zeitsignale automatisch gesteuerte Uhr geht somit bis zu

leap-second adjustment is inserted if necessary, preferably at the end of the month, preferably on December 31st, and June 30th. A leap-second is inserted between the end of the 60th second of the last minute of the last day of a month and the beginning of the following minute. The minute during which the correction is made either contain 59 or 61 seconds, depending on whether the correction was negative or positive.

If one needs a more exact UTC-time signal than ± 0.7 seconds, the difference UT1-UTC is provided by many time signal radio stations in a coded format to a resolution of 0.1 seconds. The time signal stations WWV and WWVH, for instance, transmit DUT1 information in the following way: doubling of the first through the seventh seconds pulses indicated a "plus" correction; doubling of the 9th through the 15th pulses indicates a "minus" correction. The eighth seconds pulse is not used for any code. The amount of correction in units of 0.1 second at the stations WWV/WWVH is determined by counting the number of seconds pulses that are doubled, the DUT1 is "plus 0.3 seconds." Another example: if the ninth, tenth, eleventh, twelfth, thirteenth and fourteenth seconds pulses are doubled, DUT1 is "minus 0.6 seconds." The numerical corrections to the time broadcast must be added to UTC if plus is transmitted. To obtain UT1 if minus is transmitted, the correction must be subtracted. Thus a clock remotely controlled by the time signals of a time signal radio station will be fast with respect to UT1 if a "minus" is broadcast. The corrections are revised as necessary; the new value usually

0.7 Sekunden vor, wenn ein „Minus" gesendet wird. Diese Korrekturen (DUT1) werden bedarfsweise aktualisiert. In der Regel erscheint ein neuer aktualisierter Wert erstmalig in der Stunde nach 0000 UTC.

appears for the first time during the hour after 0000 UTC.

## 4.1. Aufbau und Wirkungsweise von Atomfrequenznormalen

Grundlage für alle Arten von Atomfrequenznormalen sind stets Präzisions-Quarzoszillatoren. Der Quarzoszillator produziert die Normalfrequenz, das jeweilige Atomfrequenznormal regelt lediglich mögliche Ungenauigkeiten des Quarzoszillators aus.
Als Normalfrequenz-Generatoren stehen derzeit die vier nachfolgenden Generatortypen zur Verfügung:

| Bezeichnung | Primär- oder Sekundär- normal | Arbeits- frequenz(en) |
|---|---|---|
| Quarzgeneratoren | Sekundär | bis 100 MHz |
| Rubidium-Gaszellen-Normal | Sekundär | 6.8 ... GHz |
| Cäsiumstrahl-Normal | Primär | 9.2 ... GHz |
| Wasserstoff-Maser | Primär | 1.4 ... GHz |

Während der Quarzgenerator ein nichtatomares Normal ist, handelt es sich bei den drei anderen Typen um Atomfrequenznormale.
Der Unterschied zwischen Primär- und Sekundärnormalen besteht darin, daß Primärnormale zeitlebens keinerlei Eichung bedürfen, da sie keiner Alterung unterliegen. Sekundärnormale sind gelegentlich nachzueichen.

## 4.1. Basic Concept of Atomic Frequency Standards

In all cases of Atomic Frequency Standards generally high-performance Quartz-Crystal-Oscillators are needed for producing the standard frequency. The Atomic Frequency Standard only regulates a possible frequency driftoff of the quartz-crystal-oscillator.
The following four standard frequency oscillators can be found in practice today:

| Name | Primary or secondary Standard? | Working frequency |
|---|---|---|
| High-performance Quartz-Crystal-Oscillator | secondary | up to 100 MHz |
| Rubidium Gas-Cell Atomic Oscillator | secondary | 6.8 ... GHz |
| Cesium Beam Atomic Oscillator | primary | 9.2 ... GHz |
| Hydrogen Maser Atomic Oscillator | primary | 1.4 ... GHz |

Among these four types of standards, the quartz-crystal-oscillator is representing the only nonatomic oscillators. The frequency originating from a secondary standard can drift from time to time, while that one produced by a primary standard can be seen as absolutely constant throughout the standard's whole lifetime. Secondary standards therefore have to be adjusted from time to time.

13

In der Praxis kaum anzutreffen, aber dennoch erwähnenswert sind die Generatortypen:
- Ammoniak-Maser
- Methanstabilisierter Laser
- Rubidium-Gaszellen-Maser und
- Thalliumstrahl-Normal.

Auf die Funktionsweisen soll hier nicht näher eingegangen werden.

Other types of atomic frequency standards were developed in the past, but the devices described hereunder can't be found in any practical use:
- Ammonia Maser
- Methane Stabilized Laser
- Rubidium Gas-cell Maser
- Thallium Beam Tube.

The concept of these standards will not be declared, as anyhow it is similar to those explained lateron.

## 4.2. Quarz-Oszillatoren (XO)

Die Wirkungsweise eines in einem Oszillator eingebauten Quarzes kann etwa mit der einer akustischen Stimmgabel verglichen werden:

Eine Stimmgabel benötigt mechanische Energie (einen Anstoß), um auf einer den Maßen der Stimmgabel entsprechenden Frequenz zu schwingen. Um die Stimmgabel im Schwingungszustand zu halten, muß ständig mechanische Energie von außen nachgeführt werden.

Ein Schwingquarz schwingt je nach seiner Größe und der Art des Quarzschnittes auf einer (oder mehreren) Frequenz(en). Um ihn zum Schwingen anzuregen, muß auch hier Energie (elektrischer Art) zugeführt werden. Die Resonanzfrequenz eines Quarzes ist sehr konstant (bis zu $10^{-10}$), kann sich aber alterungs- und temperaturbedingt ändern.

Während der Alterungseffekt durch sogenannte Nachziehkapazitäten (in der Regel Kapazitätsdioden) bis zu bestimmten Grenzen ausgeglichen werden kann, gleicht man die Temperaturabhängigkeit auf verschiedene Arten aus:

Bei einem temperaturkompensierten Quarzoszillator (TCXO) wird die Temperatur des Quarzes mit einem Sensor gemessen und die bekannte Temperaturdrift elektrisch ausgeglichen.

Bei einem thermostatkontrollierten Quarzoszillator (OCXO) wird die Temperatur des Quarzes von außen her konstant gehalten.

## 4.2. High-performance quartz-crystal-oscillators

The function of a quartz-crystal built into an electrical oscillator nearly can be compared with the function of an acustical tuning-fork.

A tuning-fork needs mechanical energy (a short impulse) to vibrate on a frequency which depends on the tuning-forks size. To keep the tuning-fork vibrating, constantly more mechanical energy must be offered to it.

Depending on the quartz' size and kind of cutting it oscillates on one (or several) frequency(ies). To stimulate the quartz' oscillation, again energy has to be supplied (electrical energy this time).

The quartz resonance frequency is very constant (down to $10^{-10}$), but it can drift away on aging and temperature effects.

Within a limited frequency range, the aging effect can be compensated with the helpf of capacity diodes. The temperature conditions can be compensated in different ways:

In the case of a temperature compensated quartz-crystal oscillator (TCXO) the quartz' temperature is measured with a sensor, and the quartz' known temperaturedrifting is compensated electrically.

Within an oven controlled quartz-crystaloscillator (OXCO), the quartz is placed into a thermostate that keeps the quartz on a constant temperature.

Most of the high-precision oscillators contain a voltage controlled quartz-

Am häufigsten anzutreffen sind bei Präzisionsoszillatoren spannungsstabilisierte Quarzoszillatoren (VCXO). Ein VCXO ist ein OCXO, dem von außen im Fall einer festgestellten Abweichung eine Regelspannung zur Kapazitätsdiode zugeführt wird.

crystal-oscillator (VCXO); a VCXO is an OXCO which additionally is compensated electrically if a driftoff is measured from outside the quartz.

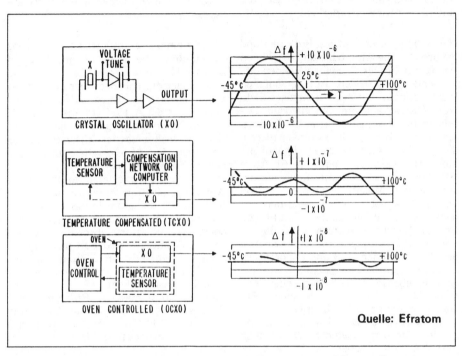

Quelle: Efratom

Die Klassen der Quarz-Oszillatoren

Main Categories of Quartz Crystal Oscillators (Efratom)

## 4.3. Rubidium-Gaszellen-Normal

In einem Rb-Gaszellen-Normal werden Vorgänge in der Atomhülle des Rubidium-Atoms zur Nachregelung eines Quarzoszillators (VCXO) genutzt.
Hierzu sind nähere Betrachtungen des Rubidium-Atoms erforderlich:

Der Atomkern besteht aus Protonen und Neutronen. Die Atomhülle umfaßt 87 den Atomkern auf verschiedenen Bahnen umkreisenden Elektronen. Auf der äußeren Bahn befindet sich nur ein einziges Elektron. Dieses kann drei verschiedene Zwischenbahnen (im Bild mit A bis C dargestellt) einnehmen, die exakt festliegen. Je nach dem Abstand der Zwischenbahn zum Atomkern zeichnet das Rb-Atom sich durch ganz bestimmte Energieunterschiede aus. Möchte man das Elektron von Bahn A nach Bahn C befördern, so geht das nur durch äußere Zufuhr von Energie. Kehrt es von Bahn C nach Bahn B oder A zurück, so gibt das Atom Energie ab. Da die Bahnen A, B und C exakt festliegen, erfolgt die Energiezufuhr und -abgabe in ebenso exakt festliegenden Portionsgrößen („Quanten"). In einem Rb-Gaszellen-Normal wird Energie in Form von Lichtstrahlen aus einer Spektrallampe den Atomen zugeführt. Ursprünglich befinden sich — über die Masse vieler Rb-Atome betrachtet — gleichviele Elektronen auf Bahn A wie auf Bahn B. Mit Hilfe spezieller Filter werden nur die Elektronen, die sich auf Bahn A befinden, angeregt, die Bahn C einzunehmen. Von Bahn C kehrt das Elektron selbsttätig nach kurzer Zeit auf Bahn A oder B zurück. Bei erneuter Betrachtung einer Vielzahl von Rb-Atomen stellt man fest, daß zunächst etwa gleichviele Atome mit Elektronen auf Bahn A und Bahn B vorliegen, infolge der Filterwirkung erfolgt jedoch bald eine Anreicherung der Gattung „A". Dabei erhält die Fotozelle hinter der Resonanzzelle weniger Lichtenergie, da hierzu Licht benötigt wird.

## 4.3. The Rubidium Gas-Cell Standard

In a Rubidium Gas-Cell Standard the ground-state hyperfine transition of the Rubidium-Atom is utilized to control the frequency of a quartz-crystal oscillator (VCXO). Some further explnations are necessary:

The Rubidium atom owns 87 electrons surrounding the nucleon on different orbits. The outer orbit contains one lonely electron. This electron can surround the nucleon on three different suborbits (named A to C in the diagram). Depending on the distance to the nucleon, that electron possesses different energy potentials for each of these three suborbits. To lift the lectron from A to C, energy has to be offered to the atom. When the electron is returning from C to B or A, the atom looses energy. As the orbits A, B and C are absolutely constant, the atom absorbs or offers energy in always fixed portions ("quantities"). In practise in a Rubidium Gas-Cell Standard energy is pumped into the atom by means of light.
Looking on a mass of Rb-atoms we'll find as many atoms with an "A"-status as with a "B"-status (fig. 1). With the help of special optical filters only electrons on sub-orbit "A" are excited to move to "C" (fig. 2), but after a short moment some of them fall back to level A and B independently (fig. 3). If again energy is offered to the atoms, some of the "A"s move to "C" etc. until all electrons will have reached level "B" (fig. 8).
If some atoms next are returning to level A, again light will be absorbed, and the intensity of the light beam will drop sharply. This is done by irradiating the atoms with the radio frequency of exactly 6.834 682 641 GHz. Now we have reached the origin (fig. 1) and the optical pumping can start again.
The optical pumping and the changing of the levels within the atoms of course

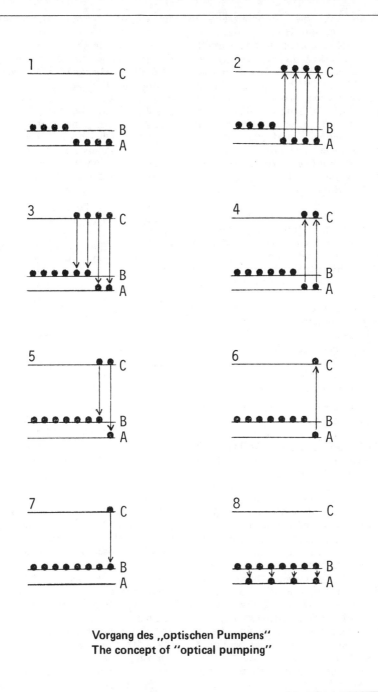

**Vorgang des ,,optischen Pumpens''**
**The concept of ''optical pumping''**

Angeordnet ist die Resonanzzelle in einem sogenannten Hohlraumresonator. Wird dem Hohlraumresonator magnetische Energie von exakt 6.834 682 641 GHz zugeführt, so begeben sich Elektronen von Bahn A auf Bahn B, bis eine gleichmäßige A-B-Verteilung erreicht und damit der ursprüngliche Zustand wiederhergestellt ist. Nun kann erneut das optische Pumpen beginnen, und die Fotozelle erhält erneut weniger Licht.

Das optische Pumpen durch die Spektrallampe und die Elektronenumverteilung durch Anregung mit 6.834... GHz geschieht in jedem Rb-Atom zwar nacheinander, bei Betrachtung der Masse aller vorhandenen Atome aber gleichzeitig. Benötigt wird zur Erzeugung der Resonanzfrequenz von 6.834...GHz ein Quarzoszillator, der durch Vervielfachung Frequenzteilungen und Mischung diese Frequenz erzeugt. Ob die Resonanzfrequenz präzise erreicht ist, läßt sich an zwei Stellen messen, denn nur im Resonanzfall erreicht

a) die Lichtmenge an der Fotozelle ihr Minimum und
b) die von der Resonanzzelle aufgenommene Energie ihr Maximum.

Woher weiß aber der Fotodetektor bzw. die Resonanzzelle, daß das Minimum bzw. Maximum erreicht ist?! Hierzu läßt man die Resonanzfrequenz 6.834 682 641 GHz absichtlich mit 127 Hz (bei manchen Geräten auch 82 oder 137 Hz) pendeln. Ist die gewünschte Resonanzfrequenz erreicht, so kann der Fotozelle ein Strom mit 2 x 127 Hz (bzw. 137 Hz) = 254 Hz (bzw. 274 Hz) entnommen werden. Liegt die Resonanzfrequenz unter oder über dem Soll, so sind an der Fotozelle 127 Hz (bzw. 137 Hz) meßbar. Auch das „unter" bzw. „über" kann meßtechnisch unterschieden werden, da die Phasen des 127 Hz- (bzw. 137 Hz-) Signals sich im Unter- und Überschreitungsfall jeweils um 180° in der Phasenlage voneinander unterscheiden. Um über das Minimum/Maximum zu pendeln, könnte man jede beliebige Pendelfrequenz wählen. Um so verwunderlicher erscheint daher die auf

appears step by step, but looking onto a mass of Rb-atoms, the whole thing is occurring contemporaneously.

For producing the resonance frequency of 6.834 ... GHz a VCXO is needed. For testing if the synthesized VCXO-frequency indeed is correct, two technical possibilities are available:

a) by measuring the light current at the photo cell (should have a minimum in the resonance case) and
b) by measuring the energy absorbed by the resonance cell (should have a maximum in the resonance case).

But how does the photo cell respectively the resonance cell recognize the point of Minimum or Maximum? To find this point, the resonance frequency is alternating 127 times per second (some Rb Standards use 82 or 137 Hz) slightly around the resonance frequency. If the resonance frequency exactly has been reached, the frequency of the photocell's current has a frequency of 2 x 127 Hz (respectively 137 Hz) = 254 Hz (respectively 274 Hz). Is the frequency lower or higher than the resonance frequency, 127 Hz (respectively 137 Hz) can be measured at the photocell. Even the "lower" or "higher" can be recognized, because the phases in both cases are differing by 180°.

To find the minimum/maximum, generally any frequency could be chosen; the choice of 82, 127 or 137 Hz therefore should be rather astonishing: Any of these three frequencies neither corresponds to the line frequency of 50 Hz (Europe), 60 Hz (USA), nor to a harmonic of 50 Hz or 60 Hz nor to any frequency used in any technical device (e.g. aircraft, satellite etc.) as far as known today. As mentioned before, Rb Standards are secondary standards. A recalibration is necessary from time to time.

The accuracy of a Rb Standard is better than $10^{-13}$. It depends on the light's intensity, the components of the buffer gas, the temperature and other effects. Rb Standards can be constructed in

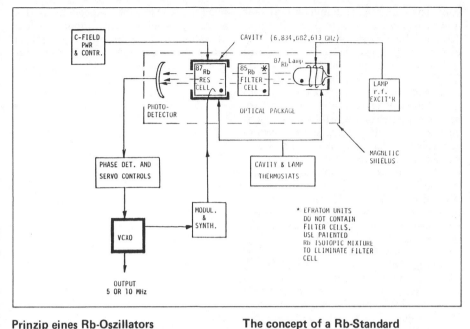

**Prinzip eines Rb-Oszillators**          **The concept of a Rb-Standard**
**(Quellen: Efratom)**

**Ein kompakter Rb-Oszillator**          **A smallsized Rb-Standard**
**Foto: Efratom**

den ersten Blick eigentümliche und sehr ungerade Frequenz von 127 Hz bzw. 137 Hz. Der Grund für diese beiden Frequenzen liegt darin, daß sie weder zu den in Europa üblichen Netzfrequenzen von 50 Hz, noch zu den in den USA üblichen Netzfrequenz von 60 Hz in einem harmonischen Verhältnis stehen und somit unerwünschte Beeinflussungen nicht zu erwarten sind. Zudem haben Messungen ergeben, daß 127 Hz und 137 Hz in keinem sonstigen technischen Gerät (z. B. im Flugzeug, in Satelliten usw.) vertreten sind.

Wie bereits aus der Tabelle ersichtlich, handelt es sich bei Rubidium-Gaszellen-Normalen um Sekundär-Normale, sie bedürfen folglich einer gelegentlichen Nacheichung. Die Genauigkeit von Rb-Gaszellen-Normalen liegt bei etwa $10^{-13}$. Sie hängt stark vom Zusammenspiel mehrerer Elemente des Rb-Normals ab, wie z. B. der Stärke des Lichts der Spektrallampe, der Gaszusammensetzung, der Temperatur und anderer Faktoren.

Rubidium-Gaszellen-Normale können sehr klein aufgebaut werden, eignen sich daher insbesondere für Zeit- und Frequenz-Normale in Flugzeugen, Satelliten oder anderer Fahrzeuge sowie in TV-Sendern (,,Präzisions-Offset'').

small sizes. They are especially used in aircrafts, satellites or other vehicles as well as in TV-transmitters (''precision offset'') or for geodesy or mobile time reference purposes.

## 4.4. Cäsium-Strahl-Normale

Bei einem Cäsium-Strahl-Normal wird ein dünner Strahl verdampfender Cäsium-Atome durch zwei Blenden in Richtung auf ein Magnetpaar (hier mit „A" bezeichnet) gelenkt. Cäsium mit dem Atomgewicht 133 besitzt in der äußeren Atomhülle ein einzelnes freies Elektron. Dieses Elektron weist eine Eigendrehung auf, wobei bei einer Vielzahl von Cs-Atomen etwa gleichviele Elektronen mit Rechtsspin (wir nennen sie nachfolgend die „R's"), wie mit Linksspin (nachfolgend: die „L's") anzutreffen sind.

Durchläuft das verdampfende Metallgas das Magnetpaar „A" mit zirka 100 m/sec, so trennen sich die weiteren Bahnen der Atome entsprechend der Richtung der Drehung des vorgenannten Elektrons: Die Atome mit den L's treffen auf einen Teilchenfänger (oder auch „Getter" genant). Sie sind für unsere weitere Betrachtung uninteressant. Die mit den R's durchlaufen einen Hohlraumresonator — das ist eine luftleere Glasröhre, in die eine elektromagnetische Welle eingekoppelt werden kann. Koppelt man exakt 9,192 631 770 GHz in diesen Hohlraumresonator, so ändert sich bei einem großen Teil der R's der Spin in die umgekehrte Richtung — es entstehen L's!

Um festzustellen, ob tatsächlich 9,192 ... GHz in den Hohlraumresonator eingespeist worden ist, trennt man am Ausgang des Hohlraumresonators die R's von den L's erneut mit einem Magnetpaar („B"). Nun sind die R's für uns ohne Bedeutung, wir wollen ja wissen, ob möglichst viele L's im Hohlraumresonator entstanden sind, was nur der Fall sein kann, wenn wir die Resonanzfrequenz 9,192... GHz exakt eingestellt haben. Wir führen daher die R's einem weiteren Teilchenfänger zu und messen mit Hilfe eines Elektronenvervielfachers und eines Strahlstrommeßgeräts die Zahl der L's.

Da man auch hier nie exakt weiß, ob und wann das Maximum des Teilchenstromes (= die Mitte der Resonanzfrequenz) er-

## 4.4. The Caesium Beam Standard

In a Caesium Beam Standard a thin beam of evaporated Caesium atoms are directed through a collimator towards a state-selector magnet (called "A" in the figure). Caesium with the atomic weight 133 possesses one lonely electron on its outer electron orbit. This lonely electron is rotating around its axis. If watching a mass of Caesium atoms, approx. 50 percent of them are possessing an outer electron with a rightspin (following this we call this kind of atoms the "R"s), and about 50 percent of them possesses an outer electron with a leftspin (following: the "L"s).

When the evaporating metalgas passes the magnet "A" with an approximate speed of 300 ft/sec, the further route of the atoms is depending on the spin of their outer electrons: The L's are kept by a getter; they aren't of interest to us. The R's pass a microwave cavity, that is a vacuum chamber into which a radio frequency wave can be coupled into. If exactly 9,192 631 770 GHz is inserted into the cavity, a great part of the R's is becoming L's now; the rotation direction of their outer electrons is changing!

For testing if indeed 9,192 ... GHz are coupled into the microwave cavity, at the end of the cavity again a state-selector magnet ("B") is sharing the R's from the L's. Now the R's are of less interest to us, because we want to get a verification that with the help of the incoupled microwave many L's were born inside the cavity. The R's are lead into another getter, and with an electron multiplier and a mass spectrometer the intensity of the L's is measured.

As nobody knows if and when the maximum of the intensity has been reached (= the centre of the resonance frequency), one again lets oscillate the resonance frequency 127 (or 82 or 137) times per second around the supposed resonance frequency. For further details see the

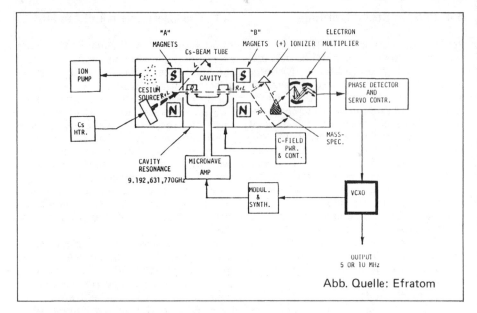

Abb. Quelle: Efratom

**Das Funktionsprinzip eines Cäsiumstrahl-Normals**
**Basic Cesium-Beam Oscillator Concept**

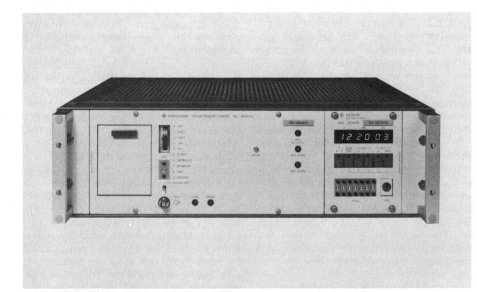

**Ein Cäsiumstrahl-Normal (Rohde & Schwarz)**
**A Cesium Beam Standard (Rohde & Schwarz)**

reicht ist, läßt man wie beim Rb-Gaszellen-Normal die Resonanzfrequenz mit 127 Hz (bzw. 82 oder 137 Hz) um die Mittenfrequenz leicht pendeln.

Cäsium-Strahl-Normale sind Primär-Normale, bedürfen daher zeitlebens keiner Nacheichung.

Bei Cs-Normalen kann eine Genauigkeit von bis zu $10^{-14}$ erreicht werden.

Cs-Normale finden Anwendung in Laboren sowie in größeren Fahrzeugen (z. B. Schiffen oder Unterseebooten).

description of the Rubidium Gas Cell Standard, please.

Caesium Beam Standards are classified as primary standards as they don't require any recalibration through their whole life.

The frequency accuracy of Caesium Beam Standards is better than $10^{-14}$.

Cs Standards are used in laboratories (e.g. Standard Frequency and Time Signal Stations) as well as in larger vehicles (e.g. ships or submarines).

## 4.5 Wasserstoff-Maser

Ein Wasserstoff-Maser (auch kurz H-Maser genannt) ist derzeit nur als Laborgerät anzutreffen. Maser steht dabei für „Microwave amplification by stimulated emission of radiation" oder zu deutsch „Mikrowellen-Verstärkung und -Erzeugung durch angeregte Strahlungsaussendung". Wenngleich die Kurzzeitgenauigkeit (1 sec bis 1 Tag) von H-Masern besser ist als bei allen anderen Standards, so ist der Aufbau dennoch relativ einfach.

Genutzt wird die Tatsache, daß das Elektron des Wasserstoff-Atoms — wie beim Cs-Atom — zwei verschiedene Eigendrehungen und damit zwei verschiedene Energiegehalte besitzen kann. Die Resonanzfrequenz beträgt hier exakt 1,420 405 751 GHz. Das Ganze kann auf zwei verschiedene Weisen in der Praxis realisiert werden:

### 4.5.1. Aktiver H-Maser

Einem Wasserstoff-Behälter wird molekularer Wasserstoff ($H_2$) entnommen und in einem Hochfrequenzfeld in atomaren Wasserstoff aufgespalten. Der atomare Wasserstoff durchströmt ein Magnetfeld, das die H-Atome hinsichtlich ihrer Energiegehalte (= Drehrichtung der Elektronen) trennt. Die Atome mit hohem Energiegehalt (H+) gelangen in einen Hohlraumresonator, die mit niedrigem Energiegehalt (H–) pumpt man ab. Sind stets genügend „H+"-Atome im Hohlraumresonator, so entsteht ein selbstschwingender atomarer Oszillator mit der Frequenz 1.4 ... GHz. Diese Frequenz kann über eine Auskoppelschleife dem Hohlraumresonator entnommen und durch Abmischen und Frequenzteilung auf 5 oder 10 MHz herabgesetzt werden.

## 4.5 The Hydrogen-Maser

When editing this book, the Hydrogen-Maser (short: H-Maser) only could be found in stationary use in laboratories. Maser stands for „Microwave amplification by stimulated emission of radiation".

The short term stability (i.e. 1 sec to 1 day) of a H-Maser is better than the short term stability of any other known standards, but nevertheless its construction is relatively simple. In a H-Maser the effect of the electron's spin — see also the Cs-Beam Standard — is utilized: The hydrogen's electron can possess two different rotation directions, and as a result of this two different energy status. The resonance frequency in a H-maser is exactly 1,420 405 751 GHz. In practise H-Masers are constructed in the following two manners:

### 4.5.1. Active H-Maser

Molecular hydrogen ($H_2$) coming from a pure hydrogen source is dissociated into atomic hydrogen ($H_1$) when passing an electrical discharge. The atomic hydrogen next is collimated into a beam, which passes a state selector magnet. H-atoms own one only electron. The electron is rotating around its axis with a left- or rightspin, and — depending on the kind of spin — the atoms contain different electrical potentials. The state selector magnet only allows the H-atoms with the higher electrical potential (H+) to enter into a coated bulb placed in a magnetic shielded resonancy cavity. The H-atoms with the lower electrical potential (H–) are directed into a getter pump; they are not of any interest to us.

If enough H+-atoms are filled into the cavity, a self sustaining microwave oscillation with the resonance frequency 1,4 ... GHz in the bulb occurs. This frequency can be coupled out with a microwave coupler, and after amplification, frequency dividing and synthesizing, a high stable frequency of 5 or 10 MHz can be got.

### 4.5.2. Passiver H-Maser

Der passive H-Maser arbeitet vom Grundsatz her wie der aktive H-Maser mit der folgenden Ausnahme: In den Hohlraumresonator wird die von einem Quarzoszillator nach erfolgtem Mischens und Vervielfachens erzeugte Resonanzfrequenz 1.4 ... GHz eingespeist. Der mit ,,H+''-Atomen gefüllte Hohlraumresonator wirkt dabei wie ein Filter und Verstärker. Nur die Resonanzfrequenz läßt der Hohlraumresonator an die Auskoppelschleife durch.

Mit H-Masern läßt sich eine Genauigkeit von bis zu $10^{-15}$ erzielen.

### 4.5.2. Passive H-Maser

A passive H-Maser nearly acts in the same manner like an active H-Maser except of the following things: The multiplied and sythenzised frequency of a quartz-crystal oscillator (VCXO) of 1,4 ... GHz is brought into the resonance cavity described above. In this case the H+-atoms inside the coated bulb act as a filter and amplifier. They only let pass the precise resonance frequency of 1,4 ... GHz to the microwave coupler installed at the opposite side of the bulb.

The H-Maser's accuracy is better than $10^{-15}$.

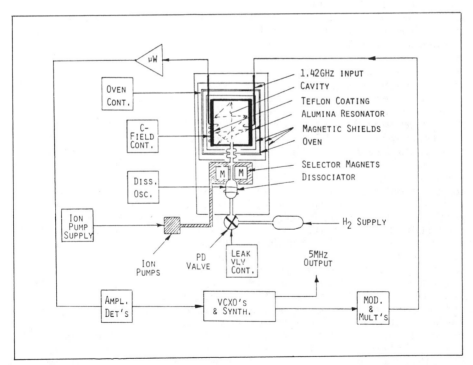

**Passiver H-Maser**
**A passive H-Maser**

Abb. Quelle: Efratom

## 5. Zeitvergleiche

Jede Uhr produziert eine Zeit. Sie mag noch so genau sein, dennoch unterliegt die von ihr produzierte Zeit irgendwelchen technisch bedingten äußerst geringen Zeitschwankungen, die nur durch Vergleich mit anderen Uhren festgestellt werden können.

Atomuhren arbeiten über den ganzen Globus verteilt. Sie sind miteinander zu vergleichen und zu koordinieren.

Der Vergleich kann über den Funkweg geschehen. Nutzt man dazu die Kurzwelle, so bringen die erheblichen und nicht berechenbaren Funkausbreitungen durch die Schwankungen der Ionosphäre eher noch zusätzliche Ungenauigkeiten ins Spiel. Die Kurzwelle ist somit für Uhrenvergleiche ungeeignet. Besser geeignet sind die Funksignale im Längstwellenbereich, die so gut wie keinen ionosphärischen Schwankungen ausgesetzt sind. Die Signale breiten sich im Längstwellenbereich auf dem kürzestmöglichen Weg per Bodenwelle vom Sender zum Empfänger aus.

Auch hier sind aber technische Grenzen gesetzt — da die im Längstwellenbereich arbeitenden Zeitzeichensender keine gigantischen Sendeleistungen haben, können sie nicht weltweit empfangen werden.

Hochleistungssender im Längstwellenbereich, die Quasi-Zeitsignale aussenden und fast über die ganze nördliche Erdhalbkugel verteilt sind, stellt das LORAN-C-Navigationssystem. Zum Zeitvergleich nutzten die Labore der Nordhalbkugel daher gelegentlich diese ständig empfangbaren LORAN-C-Impulse (100 kHz).

In der täglichen Praxis wird der Uhrenvergleich per Flugzeug realisiert! Es werden transportable Rubidium-Gaszellen-Normale (manchmal auch Cs-Normale) in Einklang mit einem stationären Cs-Normal gebracht und per Jet in möglichst kurzer Zeit zu einem (oder zwei benachbarten) Cs-Normal(en) transportiert. Dort wird das Rb-Normal, das z.B. die „Zeit" seiner Heimatstation „A" besitzt, örtlich mit Station „B" (und ggf. „C") verglichen und möglichst schnell wieder zum Ur-

## 5. Time Transfer

Every clock is producing a time. It may work very precisely, nevertheless the clock's time will waver within very small limits due to any technical reasons. These variations only can be measured by comparing a clock with other clocks.

Atomic standards are in operation all over the globe. They are to be compared and coordinated with each other. The comparison can be realized wirelessly. If one uses the shortwave, the considerable and uncalculatable variations in the ionosphere are adding further inaccurations into the game of comparision. The shortwave bands are unfit for this purpose. The VLF bands are much better usable as radiowaves transmitted on VLF are less influenced by the ionosphere. Furthermore VLF-signals are reaching any receiver on the shortest route ever possible, — by groundwave! Even here technical limits will raise soon, — timesignal stations operating in the VLF-bands don't use so highpowered transmitters that enable the listeners to pick up their signals worldwide.

Highpowered VLF radiostations which transmit quasi-timesignals are the transmitters of the LORAN-C navigation system. LORAN-C stations are covering most parts of the northern hemisphere, and time signal laboratories occasionally use(d) these LORAN-C pulses on 100 kHz for time transfer purposes.

In common practise, time transfer is realized by airplane! Portable Rubidium-Gas-Cell Standards are to be synchronized to a stationary Cs-Standard (let's say in laboratory "A") and by jet airplane the Rb Standard — containing lab A's time signals — is brought — let's say — to lab B (sometimes to a neighboured lab C too) where the Rb Standard's time signals are compared with lab B's (and C's) stationary Cs-Standard.

Finally the portable Rb Standard is transported back to its homelab for another check with the stationary Cs Standard to find out if there has occurred a time driftoff during the journey.

sprungslabor „A" zurücktransportiert, um festzustellen, ob während der Reise das Rb-Normal zeitlich abgedriftet ist.

Dazu ein willkürlich gewähltes Beispiel mit runden Zahlenwerten, das die Arbeitsweise verständlicher macht:
Die Zeit des Labors beim PTB in Braunschweig (DCF77) soll mit den Zeiten beim US Naval Observatory (USNO) in Washington und dem National Research Council (NRC) in Ottawa, Kanada (CHU) verglichen werden. Zunächst wird dazu ein beim PTB in Betrieb genommenes Rb-Standard mit der stationären Uhrengruppe verglichen. Die Zeitabweichung $\Delta t_1$ betrage 300,00 $\mu$s. Danach geht das transportable Rb-Normal sofort auf die Reise nach Washington, wo es 15 Stunden später mit dem dortigen stationären Standard verglichen wird. Die gemessene Abweichung $\Delta t_{USNO}$ möge 800,00 $\mu$s betragen. Die Reise geht weiter zum NRC-Labor in Ottawa, wo 30 Stunden nach dem Start in Braunschweig der Uhrenvergleich durchgeführt werden möge. Gemessene Abweichung dort: $\Delta t_{NRC}$ = 120,00 $\mu$s. Damit ist die Reise aber noch nicht beendet, denn sehr entscheidend für die Zuverlässigkeit des transportablen Rb-Standards ist jetzt noch der abschließende unverzügliche erneute Uhrenvergleich an der Heimatuhr beim PTB, bei der die Reise begann.
Dort möge die Abweichung 50 Stunden nach Reiseantritt $\Delta t_2$ = 300,05 $\mu$s betragen. Das bedeutet, daß im transportablen Rb-Standard seit Beginn der Reise eine Abweichung von $\Delta t_2 - \Delta t_1$ = 300,05 $\mu$s − 300,00 $\mu$s = 0,05 $\mu$s (entsprechend 50 Nanosekunden) entstanden ist.
Unterstellen wir, daß die Abweichung von 50 ns nicht plötzlich aufgetreten ist, sondern sich kontinuierlich während der 50stündigen Reise aufgebaut hat, so müßte das Rb-Standard zum Zeitpunkt des Zeitvergleichs beim USNO 15h/50h x 50 ns = 15 ns und zum Zeitpunkt des Zeitvergleichs beim NRC 30h/50h x 50 ns = 30 ns Abweichung von der zu Reiseantritt gemessenen Zeit besessen haben.

To explain the whole procedure, we have constructed an example with even numbers:
The time of the PTB Braunschweig (DCF77) is to be compared with the times of the US Naval Observatory (USNO) in Washington and with the National Research Council (NRC) in Ottawa (CHU). For starting the tour, the PTB switches on a portable Rb Standard and synchronizes it to its stationary Cs clock-group. The time of the Rb Standard ($\Delta t_1$) may differ to the official PTB-time by − let's say − 300.00 $\mu$s. Now immediately the Rb Standard is brought by jetplane to the USNO where it is compared with the USNO-clock 15 hours after the journey's beginning. The deviation to the USNO-clock $\Delta t_{USNO}$ may be measured − let's say − as 800.00 $\mu$s. The journey towards Ottawa immediately has to be continued. 30 hours after the journey's beginning, the deviation of the Rb Standard's time in relation to the NRC-clock may be $\Delta t_{NRC}$ = 120.00 $\mu$s. The Rb Standard's final route leads back to Braunschweig where another check with the PTB's stationary clock group is necessary: 50 hours after the journey's start, the Rb Standard now differs by − let's say − $\Delta t_2$ = 300.05 $\mu$s from the official PTB-time. This means, that the Rb Standard within the 50-hours-journey produced an inner-deviation of $\Delta t_2 - \Delta t_1$ = 300.05 $\mu$s − 300.00 $\mu$s = 0.05 $\mu$s (i.e. 50 Nano-seconds).

If we suppose that this inner-deviation of 50 ns did not occur all over sudden, but continuously during the whole 50-hours-journey, the Rb Standard's time should have possessed an inner-deviation of 15 h/50 h x 50 ns = 15 ns when staying at the USNO and 30 h/50 h x 50 ns = 30 ns when visiting the NRC. The time scales USNO-PTB in our example therefore differ by $\Delta t_{USNO}$ + 15 ns + $\Delta t_1$ = 800 $\mu$s + 0.015 $\mu$s + 300 $\mu$s = 1100.015 $\mu$s, and the time scales NRC-PTB differ by $\Delta t_{NRC}$ + 30 ns + $\Delta t_1$ = 120 $\mu$s + 0.03 $\mu$s + 300 $\mu$s = 420.03 $\mu$s.

Die Zeitskala USNO-PTB unterscheidet sich in unserem stark vereinfachten Beispiel damit um den realen Betrag $\Delta t_{USNO}$ + 15 ns + $\Delta t_1$ = 800 $\mu$s + 0,015 $\mu$s + 300 $\mu$s = 1100,015 $\mu$s, und die Zeitskalen NRC-PTB um den realen Betrag $\Delta t_{NRC}$ + 0,03 $\mu$s + $\Delta t_1$ = 120 $\mu$s + 0,03 $\mu$s + 300 $\mu$s = 420,03 $\mu$s.

Im Zeitalter der Satellitentechnik ist der v.g. Jet durch Satelliten ersetzt worden. Zunächst begann man 1978 mit Hilfe des deutsch-französischen Fernmeldesatelliten „Symphonie" Zeitsignale innerhalb europäischer Zeitlabore und auch zwischen europäischen und nordamerikanischen Zeitlaboren auszutauschen. Der Satellit übertrug dabei nur das, was ihm von den Bodenstationen aus übermittelt worden ist, er war also rein passiv bei den Zeitvergleichen beteiligt.

Später begannen die USA, Satelliten für das sogenannte „Global Positioning System" (GPS) auf polare Umlaufbahnen zu bringen. Die Umlaufbahnen verlaufen in Nord-Süd-Richtung, jede Bahnebene ist um 120° zur nächsten Ebene versetzt. Pro Bahnebene sind sechs Satelliten vorhanden, die die Erde in eine Art „Vogelkäfig" einkleiden. Jeder Satellit entspricht dem Jet mit dem an Bord befindlichen Rb Normal. Der Satellit kann jedoch nicht auf den Zeittakt einer stationären Uhr eingetrimmt werden, er besitzt vielmehr einen eigenen Sender mit eigenem Zeittaktgeber. Taktdifferenzen zwischen Station A und dem Satelliten können aber gemessen werden, und diese Taktdifferenzen sind schließlich die zum Uhrenvergleich bei Station B führenden Größen. Die Satelliten des GPS arbeiten auf 1575,42 MHz und 1227,6 MHz.

Bei all den Zeitvergleichen der weltweit eingesetzten Atomuhren ergibt sich irgendwann die Frage, welche der weltweit eingesetzten Uhren denn die genaue Zeit angibt. Die Antwort auf die Frage kann nur lauten: Keine der Uhren!

Die Berechnung der sog. TAI (Temps Atomique Internationale), aus der die UTC-Zeit hergeleitet wird, erfolgt rein rechnerisch auf der Basis aller etwa

In the era of communication satellites, the jetplane was replaced by a satellite. First in 1978 they tried to transfer time signals via the French/German telecommunications satellite "Symphony" between European labs and labs in Europe and the USA. Symphony acted as a passive device as it only retransmitted signals it received from the time labs.

Lateron the USA brought satellites of the Global Positioning System (GPS) into polar orbits (the satellites' name is "NAVSTAR"). The orbits pass the globe in North-South-direction and each orbit's plain differs by 120° from the next one. Six satellites are planned for each plain, which means that finally 18 satellites will cover the globe in a kind of a birdcage. Each of these 18 NAVSTARs stands for the jetplane transporting the Rb Standard, – the NAVSTAR is a "flying clock". The satellites' clock tacts of course can't be adjusted onto a stationary standard's time tact as the satellite contains an own independently working atomic standard with an own time tact. But differences in tact between – let's go back to – lab A and the NAVSTAR-satellite can be measured, and this difference in tact finally leads to the reported time transfer when reporting the amount of difference to station B.

GPS-satellites transmit on 1575.42 MHz and 1227.6 MHz.

When comparing the times of all atomic standards all over the worlds, one is near to ask: "Which clock is the correct one?" The answer only can be: "None of them!". The calculation of the TAI (Temps Atomique Internationale) which leads to the UTC-time scale, is formed on a pure basis of calculation between all – about 100 – clocks (resp. clock groups) all over the world. With a special developed calculation program (ALGOS) a steady comparison of all global atomic standards is done by the Bureau International de l'Heure (BIH) in Paris. The BIH constantly takes notice of the standard's uncertainties and then assigns

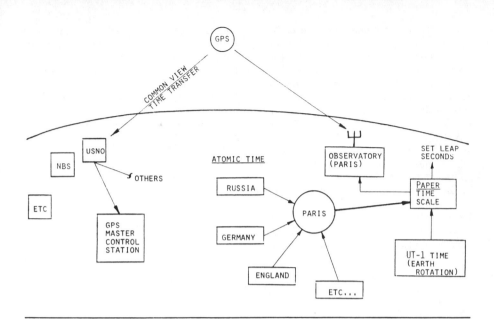

Zeitvergleiche über GPS     Time Transfer via GPS     Abbildungsquelle: Efratom

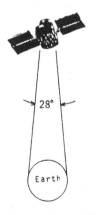

**Bahnen der 18 NAVSTAR-GPS-Satelliten**
**The orbits of the 18 NAVSTAR-GPS-**
**satellites**     **Abbildungsquelle: Efratom**

**Einer der 18 NAVSTAR-GPS-Satelliten**
**One of the 18 NAVSTAR-GPS-satellites**
    **Foto: US Airforce (Space Division)**

100 an der TAI beteiligten Cs-Uhren bzw. Uhrengruppen. Mit einem besonderen Rechenverfahren (ALGOS) ermittelt das Bureau Internationale de l'Heure (BIH) in Paris ständig die Gang-Instabilitäten der Uhren und weist ihnen dann entsprechende Bewertungsziffern zu, die sich aber laufend ändern können. Je nach Gewichtung hat ein Zeitlabor daher mit ihrer Uhr(engruppe) einen mehr oder minder gewichtigen Einfluß auf die Berechnung der TAI.

Da Zeit und Frequenz in einem direkten Verhältnis zueinander stehen, gibt die Tabelle über die Frequenzgenauigkeiten in etwa ein Bild von den Gewichtungen, die den Zeitlaboren zugemessen werden.

figures of value (weights) to them. These weights often can change. Depending on the standards' weights the labs possess a larger or smaller influence in the TAI-calcuation.

As time and frequency stand in direct relation to each other, the following table of frequency uncertainties will give you an impression of the lab's weights on TAI.

| Station | Relative Trägerungenauigkeit Relative Uncertainty of the carrier | in $10^{-10}$ |
|---|---|---|
| ATA | 0.1 | |
| BPM | 0.1 | |
| BSF | 0.2 | |
| CHU | 0.05 | |
| DCF77 | 0.005 | |
| EBC | 0.1 | |
| GBR | 0.02 | |
| HBG | 0.005 | |
| IAM | 0.5 | |
| IBF | 0.1 | |
| JJY, JG2AS | 0.1 | |
| LOL1 | 0.1 | |
| MSF (60 kHz) | 0.02 | |
| MSF (HF) | 0.02 | |
| OMA (all fqs) | 0.5 | |
| RBU, RTZ | 0.05 | |
| RCH, RID, RTA, RWM | 0.5 | |
| TDF | 0.02 | |
| UNW3, UPD8, UQC3, USB2, UTR3 | 0.05 | |
| VNG | 0.1 | |
| WWV, WWVB, WWVH | 0.1 | |
| ZUO | 0.1 | |

# 6. Zeitzeichensender

# 6. Time Signal Stations

Im folgenden Kapitel sind alle zur Zeit existierenden Standardfrequenz- und Zeitzeichensender der Welt mit ihren technischen Daten aufgeführt.
Sollte der Leser Änderungen in dem Sendeschema feststellen, so ist der Autor bzw. der Verlag für eine entsprechende Information jederzeit dankbar.

The following chapter contains all standard frequency and Time Signal Stations from all over the world with all their technical data.
Whenever the reader takes notice of changes in the stations' schedules, the author and/or the publisher gratefully awaits your response.

# Argentinien:

Servicio de Hidrográfica Naval,
Observatorio Naval, Avenida Espana 2099,
1107 Buenos Aires

Stationen:
    LOL    5000 kHz
           10000 kHz
           15000 kHz
G.K.: 34° 37' S, 58° 21' W

Sendeleistung:
    2 kW

Sendezeiten:
    1100-1200, 1400-1500, 1700-1800,
    2000-2100, 2300-2400 UTC täglich

Sendeschema:
    Siehe Diagramm

# Argentina:

Servicio de Hidrográfica Naval,
Observatorio Naval, Avenida Espana 2099,
1107 Buenos Aires

Stations:
    LOL    5000 kHz
           10000 kHz
           15000 kHz
G.C.: 34° 37' S, 58° 21' W

Power:
    2 kW

Times:
    1100-1200, 1400-1500, 1700-1800,
    2000-2100, 2300-2400 UTC daily

Type of transmission:
    as given in the diagram below

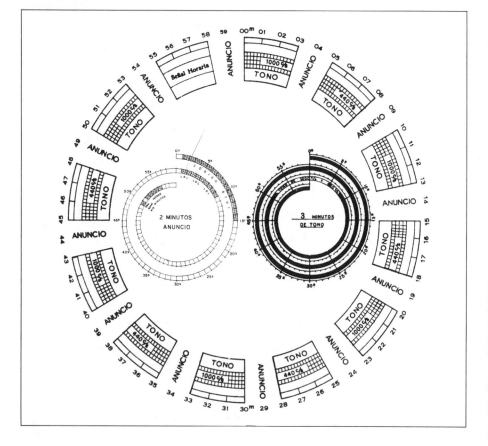

**Modulationsintervalle:** Jeweils 3 Minuten lang, beginnend in solchen Minuten, die ein Vielfaches von 5 sind, ausgenommen der 55sten Minuten. Letzteres Interval ist für die Präzisionszeitsignale vorgesehen.

**Präzisionszeitsignale:** In jeder Sekunde außer der 59sten Sekunde wird ein 5ms-Impuls ausgestrahlt, moduliert mit 1000 Hz, d. h. der Impuls besteht aus 5 Schwingungen.

**Ansage:** In der ersten Minute jeder Ansagenperiode wird der DUT1 gesendet, zu Beginn der zweiten Minute dieser Periode das Rufzeichen in Morsecode (LOL, LOL, LOL). Gegen Ende dieser Periode erfolgt eine Ansage in Sprache: Zunächst „Observatorio Naval Argentina", sodann die exakte Zeit des Momentes, in der die Modulation wieder beginnt.

DUT1:
  CCIR code durch Impulsverlängerung

Stationen:
  LOL2    4856 kHz
  LOL3    8030 kHz
  LOL3    17180 kHz

Sendezeiten:
  0100, 1300 und 2100 UTC

Sendeschema:
  A1 Sekundenimpulse in den fünf Minuten vor den v.g. Stunden. Der 29ste Sekundenimpuls jeder Minute fehlt. Die Minutenimpulse sind verlängert.

DUT1:
  CCIR code durch Impulsverdoppelung

Bestätigung:
  Falt-QSL

Servicio Internacional de la Hora, Calle 38 Gral. Nicolas Savio No. 865, 1650 Villa Maipú, San Martin, Pcia de Buenos Aires

Stationen:
  LQB 9    8167,5 kHz

  LQC20   17550,0 kHz
Anhand vorliegender unbestätigter Meldungen hat diese Station den Betrieb eingestellt.

**Modulation intervals:** 3 minutes, beginning at all the minutes which are multiples of 5, except of the 55th minute, this interval being reserved for the precision time signals.

**Precision time signal:** A 5 ms pulse is sent every second (except of the 59th one) of each minute of signal, modulation frequency 1000 Hz, i. e. it consists of 5 cycles.

**Announcements:** In the first minute of each "announcement" period the station transmits the code DUT1. At the beginning of the 2nd minute of these periods it transmits its callsign in Morse (LOL, LOL, LOL) and at the end of the period it announces the origin of the emission with the words "observatorio Naval Argentina", followed by the exact time and minute at which the text modulation will begin.

DUT1:
  CCIR code by lenghtening

Stations:
  LOL2    4856 kHz
  LOL3    8030 kHz
  LOL3    17180 kHz

Times:
  0100, 1300 und 2100 UTC

Type of transmission:
  A1 second pulses during the 5 minutes preceding the above time. Second 29 is omitted. Minute pulses are prolonged.

DUT1:
  CCIR code by double pulse.

V.
  by QSL folder

Servicio Internacional de la Hora, Calle 38 Gral. Nicolas Savio No. 865, 1650 Villa Maipú, San Martin, Pcia de Buenos Aires

Stations:
  LQB 9    8167,5 kHz

  LQC20   17550,0 kHz
According to unconfirmed information, this station seems to have ceased operation.

## Australien

National Standards Commission
P.O.Box 282
North Ryde
NSW 2113

Stationen:
  6449 kHz
  12982 kHz

Sendeleistung:
  10 kW

G.K.: $35^O$ 12' S, $149^O$ 06' Ost
Nahe Belconnen

Sendezeit: ständig

Modulation: A2

Sendeschema:
  Die Station sendet 50 ms lange Sekundenimpulse mit 1000 Hz Modulation; die Sekundenimpulse 55 bis 58 sind nur 5 ms lang; Impuls 59 fehlt; der Minutenimpuls ist 0.5 sek lang. Während den 5., 10., 15. (usw.) Minuten sind die Sekundenimpulse 50 bis 58 nur 5 ms lang.

DUT1:
  Während der 15 ersten Sekunden jeder Minute. Den normalen Zeitimpulsen folgt entsprechend CCIR code bei Bedarf ein 50 ms langer Impuls mit 900 Hz.

## Australia

National Standards Commission
P.O.Box 282
North Ryde
NSW 2113

Stations:
  6449 kHz
  12982 kHz

Power:
  10 kW

G.C.: $35^O$ 12' S, $149^O$ 06' E
Near Belconnen

Times: continuous

Modulation: A2

Type of transmission:
  The station transmits seconds markers of 50 cycles of 1 kHz modulation; 5 cycles only for seconds markers 55 to 58; second marker 59 is omitted; and 500 cycles for the minute markers. During the 5th, 10th, 15th etc. minutes, second markers 50 to 58 only 5 cycles of 1 kHz.

The deviation of the time signals from UT1 is transmitted each minute using the CCIR code by 45 cycles of 900 Hz modulation immediately following the normal second markers.

## Brasilien:

Observatorio Nacional (CNP$_q$- National Council for Scientific and Technological Development), Time Service Division, R. General Bruce, 586, Sao Cristavao — 20921-Rio de Janeiro, RJ

Station:
  PPE 8721 kHz

G.K.: 22$^o$ 54' S, 43$^o$ 13' W

Sendeleistung:
  2 kW

Sendezeiten:
  00.30, 11.30, 13.30, 19.30, 20.30 und 23.30 UTC

Sendeschema:
  Sekundenimpulse in A1 während der fünf den o.a. Zeiten vorangehenden Minuten entsprechend dem Modern American Modified System.

DUT1:
  CCIR code mit Impulsverdoppelung

## Brazil:

Observatorio Nacional (CNP$_q$-National Council for Scientific and Technological Development), Time Service Division, R. General Bruce, 586, Sao Cristovao — 20921-Rio de Janeiro, RJ

Station:
  PPE      8721 kHz

G.C.: 22$^o$ 54' S, 43$^o$ 13' W

Power:
  2 kW

Times:
  00.30, 11.30, 13.30, 19.30, 20.30 and 23.30 UTC

Type of transmission:
  Second pulses, A1, during 5 minutes preceding the times mentioned above.

DUT1:
  CCIR code by double pulse.

## noch: Brasilien

VHF-Stationen Rio de Janeiro
und Brasllia:
VHF-1          160.230 MHz      MHz
80 Watt
Sekundenimpulse von 5 ms Länge
und 1 kHz Modulation

VHF-2          171.130 MHz
80 Watt
Alle 10 Sekunden eine Zeitansage mit
anschließendem stark modulierten Impuls

VHF-3          166.530 MHz
80 Watt
Standard Modulationsfrequenz 1000 Hz

Station PPR, Empresa Brasileira de Telecomunicaçoes S.A. (EMBRATEL),
Estrada da Matriz 2960, Guaratiba,
23.000 Rio de Janeiro, RJ

Stationen:
    435 kHz
   4244 kHz
   8634 kHz
  13105 kHz
  17194,4 kHz
  22603,0 kHz

Sendeleistungen:
  1 kW und 5 kW

G.K.: 22° 59′ S., 43° 11′ W

Modulation:
  A1

Sendezeiten:
  01.25-01.30, 14.25-14.30,
  21.25-21.30 UTC

Sendeschema:
  5 ms lange Sekundenimpulse. Die Impulse 58, 59 und 60 jeder Minute sind 200 ms lang. Gesteuert werden auch diese Zeitzeichen vom Observatorio Nacional.

## Brasilia cont.

VHF Transmissions:
Using three VHF (FM) transmitters with omnidirectional antennas, the National Observatory broadcasts time announcements and time signals daily on a continued basic. Such signals are now transmitted in Brasiiia and Rio de Janeiro.

Frequencies:
VHF-1          160.230 MHz
80 Watts
(time signals, 5 ms, modulated pulses, 1 kHz mod.)

VHF-2          171.130 MHz
80 Watts
(time announcements every 10 seconds with a maximum modulated pulse marking the time)

VHF-3          166.530 MHz
80 Watts
(standard frequency 1000 Hz)

Station PPR, Empresa Brasileira de Telecomunicaçoes S.A. (EMBRATEL),
Estrada da Matriz 2960, Guaratiba,
23.000 Rio de Janeiro, RJ

Stations:
    435 kHz
   4244 kHz
   8634 kHz
  13105 kHz
  17194,4 kHz
  22603,0 kHz

Power:
  1 kW and 5 kW

G.C.: 22° 59′ S, 43° 11′ W

Modulation:
  A1

Times:
  01.25-01.30, 14.25-14.30,
  21.25-21.30 UTC

Type of transmission:
Second pulses, during 5 ms, sent by the time service of the National Observatory. Pulses of seconds 58, 59 and 60 of every minute extend over 200 ms.

## Chile:

Instituto Hidrográfico de la Armada,
Errázuriz 232, Casilla 324, Valparaíso

Stationen:
  CBV Playa Ancha Radio
    4228 kHz
    8677 kHz

Modulation:
  A2A

Sendezeiten:
  11.55-12.00, 15.55-16.00, 19.55-20.00,
  00.55-01.00 UTC
  Vom 2. Samstag im Oktober bis zum
  2. Samstag im März eine Stunde früher.

Sendeschema:
  Modern American Modified System

Bestätigung:
  per Schreiben

## Chile:

Instituto Hidrográfico de la Armada,
Errázuriz 232, Casilla 324, Valparaíso

Stations:
  CBV Playa Ancha Radio
    4228 kHz
    8677 kHz

Modulation:
  A2A

Times:
  11.55-12.00, 15.55-16.00, 19.55-20.00,
  00.55-01.00 UTC
  From the second Saturday of October
  to the second Saturday of March,
  one hour earlier (daylight saving time)

Type of transmission:
  See the Modern American Modified
  System.

V.
  by letter, Rp

## China:

Shaanxi Astronomical Observatory,
Academia Sinica, P.O.Box 18, Lintong,
(Xian)

Stationen:
| BPM | 2500 kHz | 00.00-10.00 UT |
| | 5000 kHz | 09.00-01.00 UT |
| | 10000 kHz | 00.00-24.00 UT |
| | 15000 kHz | 01.00-09.00 UT |

Sendeleistung:
  10-20 kW

G.K.:     $35^0$ 0′ N, $139^0$ 31′ Ost

Sendeschema:
  Siehe nachfolgendes Diagramm

## China:

Shaanxi Astronomical Observatory,
Academia Sinica, P.O.Box 18, Lintong,
(Xian)

Stations:
| BPM | 2500 kHz | 00.00-10.00 UT |
| | 5000 kHz | 09.00-01.00 UT |
| | 10000 kHz | 00.00-24.00 UT |
| | 15000 kHz | 01.00-09.00 UT |

Power:
  10-20 kW

G.C.: $35^0$ 0′ N, $139^0$ 31′ E

Type of transmission:
  see the diagram below

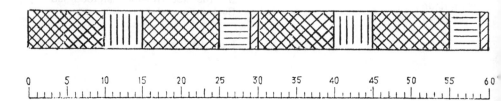

Starting at 29m 42s and 59m 42s: 10 time BPM in slow CW and 2 times
by female voice in Chinese
Beginnend um 29m 42s und 59m 42s: 10 mal BPM in Morsecode und
2 mal in chinesischer Sprache

UTC seconds and minutes pulses of 1 kHz (10 ms-/300 ms-duration)*
UTC Sekunden- und Minutenimpulse mit 1 kHz (10 ms-/300 ms-Länge)*

AO signals
Träger

UT1 seconds and minutes pulses of 1 kHz (10ms-/300ms-duration)
UT1 Sekunden- und Minutenimpulse mit 1 kHz (10 ms-/300 ms-Länge)

---

* Die Signale weichen um 0,02 s von der offiziellen UTC ab (gehen vor)
* The signals have a deviation of 0.02 s from official UTC (are advancing UTC)

| Nachfolgende Informationen über BPM sind nicht bestätigt! | The following information on BPM are unconfirmed! |
|---|---|
| **Station:**<br>BPM    5430 kHz | **Station:**<br>BPM    5430 kHz |
| **Sendezeiten:**<br>10.00, 12.00, 14.00, 16.00 und 18.00 UT | **Times:**<br>10.00, 12.00, 14.00, 16.00 and 18.00 UT |
| **Station:**<br>BPM    9351 kHz | **Station:**<br>BPM    9351 kHz |
| **Sendezeiten:**<br>06.00, 11.00, 13.00, 15.00, 17.00,<br>19.00, 21.00 und 23.00 UT | **Times:**<br>06.00, 11.00, 13.00, 15.00, 17.00,<br>19.00, 21.00 and 23.00 UT |

Nachfolgende Informationen
über BPM sind nicht bestätigt!

Station:
 BPM    5430 kHz

Sendezeiten:
 10.00, 12.00, 14.00, 16.00 und 18.00 UT

Station:
 BPM    9351 kHz

Sendezeiten:
 06.00, 11.00, 13.00, 15.00, 17.00,
 19.00, 21.00 und 23.00 UT

Sendeschema:
Die Sendungen erfolgen in den 9 Minuten vor und den 6 1/2 Minuten nach den oben angegebenen Stunden in nachfolgender Weise:

51 m 00 s − 54 m 00 s
    Rufzeichen BPM in Morse-Code
55 m 00 s − 00 m 00 s
    Tonmodulierte Sekundenimpulse
    UT 1

The following information on BPM
are unconfirmed!

Station:
 BPM    5430 kHz

Times:
 10.00, 12.00, 14.00, 16.00 and 18.00 UT

Station:
 BPM    9351 kHz

Times:
 06.00, 11.00, 13.00, 15.00, 17.00,
 19.00, 21.00 and 23.00 UT

Type of transmission:
The transmission occurs during the 9 minutes before and the 6 1/2 minutes after the hours mentioned before in the following way:

51 m 00 s − 54 m 00 s
    Morse Code BPM
55 m 00 s − 00 m 00 s
    Modulated seconds pulses UT1
00 m 10 s − 00 m 30 s
    long pips of 1000 Hz

BPM

CSAO

陕 西 天 文 台

Thank you for your reception report of BPM. This is to verify the following report:

Call __BPM__ Frequency 10 MHz

Location __109° 31' E, 35° 00' N__

Date __26/1/81__ Time __19:50 GMT__

Radiated Power __10-20 KW__

Antenna __omnidirectional__

Signature  Yang Huai-xu

Title Chief, Section of
~~Science and Technique~~

## noch: China

00 m 10 s – 00 m 30 s
  Langer Ton 1000 Hz
01 m 00 s – 06 m 00 s
  Zeitsignale
06 m 10 s – 06 m 30 s
  Langer Ton 1000 Hz

Siehe hierzu auch das nachfolgende
Diagramm

Bestätigung:
  per QSL-Karte

## China cont.

01 m 00 s – 06 m 00 s
  time signals, scientific forms
06 m 10 s – 06 m 30 s
  long pips of 1000 Hz

See also the diagram

V.
  by QSL

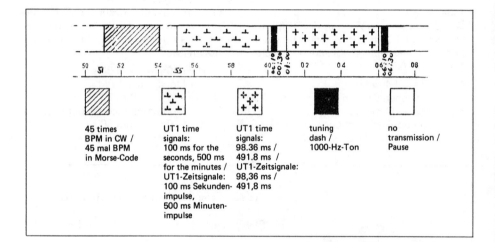

| 45 times BPM in CW / 45 mal BPM in Morse-Code | UT1 time signals: 100 ms for the seconds, 500 ms for the minutes / UT1-Zeitsignale: 100 ms Sekunden-impulse, 500 ms Minuten-impulse | UT1 time signals: 98.36 ms / 491.8 ms / UT1-Zeitsignale: 98,36 ms / 491,8 ms | tuning dash / 1000-Hz-Ton | no transmission / Pause |
|---|---|---|---|---|

## noch: China

Coastal Radio Station XSG Shanghai
Radio, Shanghai

Stationen:
    522,5 kHz
    6454 kHz
    8487 kHz
    12954 kHz
    16938 kHz

Sendezeiten:
    02.55-03.00 und 08.55-09.00 UT

Sendeschema:
    wie im nachfolgenden Diagramm dar-
    gestellt

## China cont.

Coastal Radio Station XSG Shanghai
Radio, Shanghai

Station:
    522,5 kHz
    6454 kHz
    8487 kHz
    12954 kHz
    16938 kHz

Times:
    02.55-03.00 and 08.55-09.00 UT

Type of transmission:
    as shown in the diagram

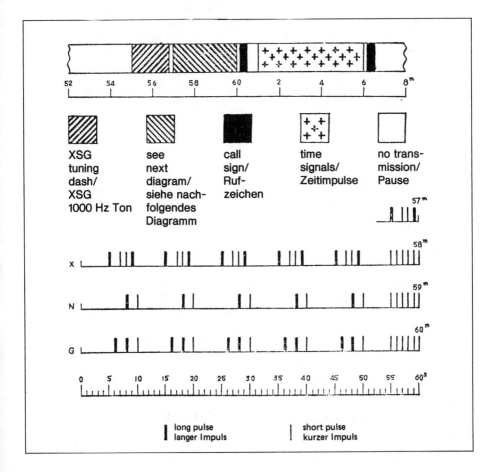

## Deutsche Demokratische Republik

Amt für Standardisierung, Meßwesen und Warenprüfung, Fachgebiet Zeit- und Frequenzdienst der DDR, Fürstenwalder Damm 388, DDR-1162 Berlin

Station:
Y3S    4525 kHz
(Senderstandort Nauen)

G. K.: $52^o$ 39′ N, $12^o$ 55′ Ost

Sendeleistung:
5 kW

Sendezeiten:
ständig, außer von 08.15 bis 09.45 UTC im Bedarfsfall für Senderwartungsarbeiten

Sendeschema:
Sekundenimpulse von 100 ms Länge, Minutenimpulse von 500 ms Länge. Die Minuten- und Stundenangaben sind außerdem in den Sekunden 41-55 jeder Minute in BCD-Code entsprechend nachstehendem Diagramm codiert.

## German Democratic Republic

Amt für Standardisierung, Meßwesen und Warenprüfung, Fachgebiet Zeit- und Frequenzdienst der DDR, Fürstenwalder Damm 388, DDR-1162 Berlin

Station:
Y3S    4525 kHz
(transmitter at Nauen)

G. C.: $52^o$ 39′ N, $12^o$ 55′ E

Power:
5 kW

Times:
continuous, except from 08.15 to 09.45 UTC for maintenance if necessary

Type of transmission:
Second pulses of 100 ms duration. Minute pulses prolonged to 500 ms. Minute and hour information also is coded in BCD-code at seconds 41 to 55 of each minute as shown in the following diagram.

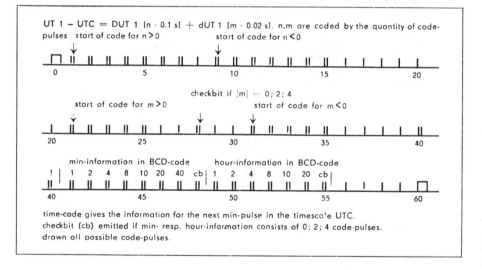

DUT1:
CCIR-Code durch Impulsverdopplung

Bestätigung:
per QSL-Faltkarte

V.
by QSL folder

# Bundesrepublik Deutschland:

Physikalisch-Technische Bundesanstalt,
Laboratorium 4.41, Bundesallee 100,
D-3300 Braunschweig

Station:
DCF77 77.5 kHz

Sendeleistung:
50 kW

Senderstandort:
Mainflingen (Nahe Frankfurt/M.)

G. K.: $50^0$ 1' N, $9^0$ 0' Ost

Sendezeit:
ständig

Modulation:
Zum Beginn jeder Sekunde (ausgenommen der 59sten) wird die Trägeramplitude für eine Dauer von 100 ms bzw. 200 ms auf etwa 25 Prozent Stärke reduziert.

Sendeschema:
Mittels einer Zeitcodierung im BCD-Code wird die in der Bundesrepublik Deutschland gültige Zeit ausgesendet, und zwar das Jahr, der Monat, der Tag, die Stunde und Minute sowie der Wochentag. Die Zeitcodierung erfolgt durch Impulslängenveränderung der Sekundenimpulse 20 bis 58 jeder Minute, wie im Diagramm ersichtlich. (100 ms = Binärschritt Null, 200 ms = Binärschritt Eins)
Ein Beispiel der Trägerhüllkurve für die Zeit 19.35 ist im nachfolgenden Bild dargestellt.

# Germany (Fed. Rep.)

Physikalisch-Technische Bundesanstalt,
Laboratorium 4.41, Bundesallee 100,
D-3300 Braunschweig

Station:
DCF77 77.5 kHz

Power:
50 kW

Location:
Mainflingen (near Frankfurt/M.)

G. C.: $50^0$ 1' N, $9^0$ 0' E

Times:
continuous

Modulation:
At the beginning of each second (except the 59th) the carrier amplitude is reduced to about 25 percent for a duration of 100 ms or 200 ms respectively.

Code:
Time code in BCD (binary coded decimal) for indicating the year, month, day, hour, minute and day of the week in the legal time of the FRG. The time code is given by pulse width modulation of second markers from marker 20 to 58 of every minute as shown in the next diagram (100 ms = binary zero, 200 ms = binary one).
An example of the carrier envelope for the coded time 1935 can be seen in the next figure.

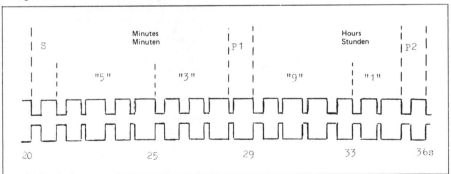

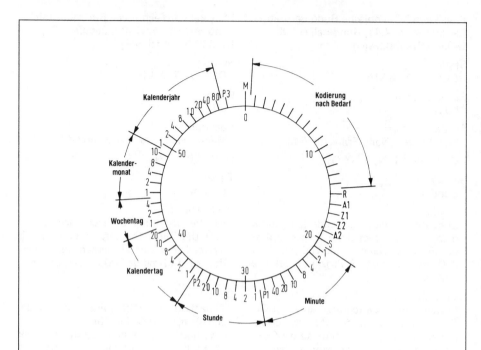

## Schema der kodierten Zeitinformation

## Coding Plan

| | | |
|---|---|---|
| P1, P2, P3 | Prüfbits | Parity check bits |
| M | Minutenmarke | minute marker (100 ms) |
| R | Aussendung erfolgt über Ausweichantenne | Second marker 15 has a duration of 200 ms if the reserve antenna is used. (This may result in a small phase time change of the carrier due to the different location of the antenna.) |
| A1 | Ankündigung für Übergang auf Sommerzeit oder zurück | Announcement of an approaching change from MEZ to MESZ or viceversa |
| S | Startbit der kodierten Zeitinformation (200 ms lang) | (second marker 20), a 200 ms marker, designates the start of the time information |
| Z1, Z2 | Während der Sommerzeit 200 ms lang; sonst 100 ms | In the case of transmission of the legal time in the form of MEZ (D) = = UTC (PTB) + 1 h second marker |
| | Während der Normalzeit 200 ms lang; Sommerzeit 100 ms | No. 18 has a duration of 200 ms and in the case of MESZ (D) = = UTC (PTB) + 2 h (summer time) second marker No. 17 is prolonged to 200 ms |
| A2 | Ankündigung einer Schaltsekunde | Announcement of a leap second |

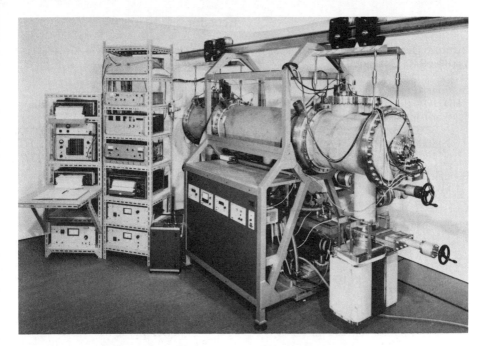

| Eine Weiterentwicklung des primären Zeit- und Frequenznormals, der Atomuhr CS1 | An improved version of the primary standard, the atomic standard CS1 |
|---|---|

## Deutschland (BR)

Das Deutsche Hydrographische Institut Hamburg hat die Ausstrahlung der Zeitzeichensendungen über die Sendestellen Elmshorn, Osterloog und Kiel (Rufzeichen: DAM/DAN/DAO) am 01. November 1985 eingestellt.

## Germany (Fed. Rep.)

The German Hydrographic Institute Hamburg has discontinued the time signal transmission via the radio stations Elmshorn, Osterloog and Kiel (call signs: DAM/DAN/DAO) on 1st November 1985.

## Ekuador:

Instituto Oceanográfico de la Armada,
Casilla 5940, Guayaquil

Stationen:
HD2IOA (lies: Hotel Delta Zwei **India**
Oskar Alpha)

| | |
|---|---|
| 3810 kHz | 05.00-17.00 UTC |
| 5000 kHz | 17.00-18.00 UTC |
| 7600 kHz | 18.00-05.00 UTC |

Sendeleistung:
1 kW

G. K.: 02° 16' S, 79° 54' W

Sendeschema:
1.) Ein-Minuten-Sendeprogramm
auf 3810 kHz und 7600 kHz:
01 s − 28 s
Impulse von 100 ms Länge
29 s
Pause
30 s − 50 s
Impulse von 100 ms Länge
51 s − 52 s
Pause

## Ecuador:

Instituto Oceanográfico de la Armada,
Casilla 5940, Guayaquil

Stations:
HD2IOA (read: Hotel Delta Two **India**
Oscar Alpha)

| | |
|---|---|
| 3810 kHz | 05.00-17.00 UTC |
| 5000 kHz | 17.00-18.00 UTC |
| 7600 kHz | 18.00-05.00 UTC |

Power:
1 kW

G. C.: 02° 16' S, 79° 54' W

Type of transmission:
1.) One minute programm on
3810 kHz and 7600 kHz:
01 s − 28 s
pulses of 100 ms omitted
29 s
omitted
30 − 50 s
pulses of 100 ms
51 s − 52 s
omitted

53 s – 58 s
Ansage in spanischer Sprache:
z. B. „Al oir el tono serán las
22 horas, 35 minutos, cero
segundos"
59 s
Pause
60 s
Impuls von 300 ms Länge

2.) Auf 5000 kHz wird gesendet:
17.00-17.15 UTC: 600 Hz Impulse
17.15-17.30 UTC: 440 Hz Impulse
17.30-18.00 UTC: Träger

3.) Zwischen 59 m 15 s und 59 m 50 s jeder Minute wird folgende Stationsansage in spanischer Sprache gesendet: „Esta es la Hora Oficial del Estado Ecuatoriano emitida por el Instituto Oceanográfico de la Armada para el territorio continental del país."

Bestätigung:
per QSL-Karte

53 s – 58 s
male voice announcement in
Spanish (e.g.: "Al oir el tono
serán las 22 horas, 35 minutos,
cero segundos.")
59 s
omitted
60 s
pulse of 300 ms duration

2.) On 5000 kHz the time is announced each minute and standard frequencies are transmitted as follows:
17.00-17.15 UTC: 600 Hz tones
17.15-17.30 UTC: 440 Hz tones
17.30-18.00 UTC: unmodulated carrier

3.) Between 59m 15s and 59m 50s the following station identication is transmitted in Spanish: "Esta es la Hora Oficial del Estado Ecuatoriano emitida por el Instituto Oceanografico de la Armada para el territorio continental del país."

V.
by QSL

# Frankreich

Die in der 10. Ausgabe des Buches Zeitzeichensender beschriebenen beiden französischen Zeitzeichenstationen FFH 2500 kHz und FTH42/FTK77/FTN87 7428 kHz/ 10775 kHz/13873 kHz haben im März 1985 die Sendungen eingestellt. Stattdessen werden hochpräzise Zeitinformationen nun über den Rundfunksender France-Inter auf 162 kHz ausgestrahlt. Näheres hierzu im Abschnitt „Rundfunksender mit hochpräzisen Zeitsignalen".

# France

The two French time signal radio stations FFH 2500 kHz and FTH42/FTK77/ FTN87 7428 kHz/10775 kHz/13873 kHz which are described in the 10th edition of Time Signal Stations ceased operation in March 1985. Instead time signals now are offered by the French broadcasting station France-Inter on 162 kHz. See the chapter „Broadcasting radio stations transmitting high-precision time signals" for further information.

## Großbritannien:

National Physical Laboratory,
Div. of Electrical Science,
Teddington, Middlesex TW11 OLW

Stationen:

| MSF | 60 kHz | 50 kW |
|-----|--------|-------|
|  | 2500 kHz | 0,5 kW |
|  | 5000 kHz | 0,5 kW |
|  | 10000 kHz | 0,5 kW |

G. K.: $52^o$ 22'N, $1^o$ 11' W

Sendezeiten:
auf 60 kHz ständig, ausgenommen an jedem ersten Dienstag des Monats von 10.00 bis 14.00 UTC (während der Sommerzeit eine Stunde früher)
auf Kurzwelle zwischen den Minuten 00-05, 10-15, 20-25, 30-35, 40-45, 50-55.

Modulation:
A2

Sendeschema:
Auf Kurzwelle: Sekundenimpulse von 5 ms Länge mit 1000 Hz Modulation, Minutenimpulse von 100 ms Länge, 1000 Hz Modulation.

0 m 00 s − 05 m 00 s
    Sekunden- und Minutenimpulse
5 m 00 s − 09 m 30 s
    Sendepause
9 m 30 s − 10 m 00 s
    Rufzeichen MSF in Morsecode

Dieses 10minütige Sendeschema wird alle 10 Minuten wiederholt.

Auf Längstwelle 60 kHz: Der Träger wird zu Beginn einer jeden Sekunde für 100 ms unterbrochen, zu Beginn einer jeden Minute für 500 ms. Während der 500 ms Unterbrechung zur vollen Minute wird im BCD NRZ Code mit einer Geschwindigkeit von 100 bit/s der Monat, die Stunde und die Minute codiert übertragen. Außerdem wird jeweils von der 17ten bis zur 59sten Sekunde jeder Minute im BCD PWM Code mit 1 bit/s das Jahr, der Monat, der Tag des Monats, der Wochentag, die Stunde und die Minute codiert übertragen.

## Great Britain:

National Physical Laboratory,
Div. of Electrical Science,
Teddington, Middlesex TW11 OLW

Stations:

| MSF | 60 kHz | 50 kW |
|-----|--------|-------|
|  | 2500 kHz | 0,5 kW |
|  | 5000 kHz | 0,5 kW |
|  | 10000 kHz | 0,5 kW |

G. C.: $52^o$ 22' N, $1^o$ 11' W

Times:
on 60 kHz continuous, except on the first Tuesday of each month from 10.00 to 14.00 UTC (during daylight saving times one hour earlier) for maintenance.
On shortwave between minutes 00-05, 10-15, 20-25, 30-35, 40-45, 50-55.

Modulation:
A2

Type of transmission:
On the shortwave service the seconds are marked by the beginning of 5 ms pulses of 1000 Hz modulation. Minutes are distinguished by 100 ms periods of modulation beginning at the minute.

The complete program is:
0 m 00 s − 05 m 00 s
    second and minute pulses
5 m 00 s − 09 m 30 s
    no radiation
9 m 30 s − 10 m 00 s
    callsign MSF repeated twice
    in slow Morse

The above 10 minute program is repeated throughout the 24 hours.
The 60 kHz time signals take the form of interruptions of the carrier of 100 ms for the second pulses, of 500 ms for the minute pulses. The signal is given by the beginning of the interruption. BCD NRZ code, 100 bit/s (month, hour, minute) during minute interruptions. BCD PWM code 1 bit/s (year, month, day of month, day of week, hour, minute) from seconds 17 to 59 in each minute.

DUT1:
CCIR Code mittels Impulsverdoppelung

Bestätigung:
per QSL-Karte

DUT1:
CCIR code by douple pulse.

V.
by QSL card, Rp preferred.

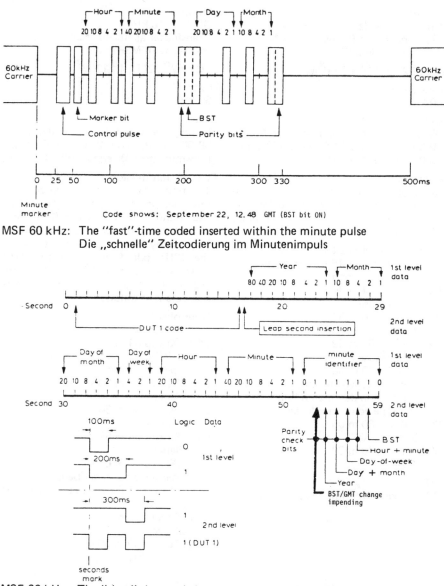

Code shows: September 22, 12.48 GMT (BST bit ON)

MSF 60 kHz: The "fast"-time coded inserted within the minute pulse
Die „schnelle" Zeitcodierung im Minutenimpuls

MSF 60 kHz: The "slow" time code between seconds 17 and 59
Die „langsame" Zeitcodierung zwischen den Sekunden 17 bis 59

Royal Greenwich Observatory,
Time Department, Herstmonceux Castle,
Hailsham, Sussex BN27 1RP

Station:
GBR    16 kHz
(Senderstandort Rugby
= Standort von MSF)

G. K.: 52° 22′ N, 1° 11′ W

Sendeleistung:
60 kW

Sendezeiten:
Während der fünf Minuten vor 03.00,
09.00, 15.00 und 21.00 UTC (GBZ nur
09.00 und 21.00 UTC)

Sendeschema:
Im Gegensatz zu MSF erfolgt eine positive Modulation. Die Sekundenimpulse sind 100 ms, die Minutenimpulse 500 ms lang.

54 m 00 s − 54 m 24 s
    GBR GBR TIME in Morsecode,
    4 mal wiederholt
54 m 24 s − 54 m 30 s
    Sendepause
54 m 30 s − 54 m 54 s
    Träger
54 m 54 s − 54 m 59 s
    Sendepause
55 m 00 s − 60 m 00 s
    Impulse wie vorstehend beschrieben.
    Der Beginn des letzten Impulses
    stellt die volle Stunde dar.
60 m 01 s − 60 m 05 s
    Sendepause
60 m 05 s − 60 m 30 s
    Träger

DUT1:
CCIR Code durch Impulsverdoppelung

---

Royal Greenwich Observatory,
Time Department, Herstmonceux Castle,
Hailsham, Sussex BN27 1RP

Station:
GBR    16 kHz
(transmitter at Rugby,
co-sited with MSF)

G. C.: 52° 22′ N, 1° 11′ W

Power:
60 kW;

Times:
During the 5 minutes preceding 03.00,
09.00, 15.00 and 21.00 UTC. (GBZ transmits at 09.00 and 21.00 UTC only).

Type of transmission:
The time signals use positive keying, the reference point being the start of carrier rise. Minute markers are 500 ms long, second markers 100 ms long. DUT1 is given by double second markers in the CCIR code: from $1^S$ to $n^S$ for DUT1 = +n x $0.1^S$, from $9^S$ to $(8+m)^S$ for DUT1 = -m x $0.1^S$. The complete schedule is as follows:

Hour plus:
    Transmission:
54 m 00 s to 54 m 24 s
    "GBR GBR TIME" in Morse
    repeated 4 times
54 m 24 s to 54 m 30 s
    silence
54 m 30 s to 54 m 54 s
    plain carrier
54 m 54 s to 54 m 59 s
    silence
55 m 00 s to 60 m 00 s
    time signals as described,
    the start of the final pulse marking
    the hour
60 m 01 s to 60 m 05 s
    silence
60 m 05 s to 60 m 30 s
    plain carrier

Das Royal Greenwich Observatory ist auch der Ursprung der in den Inlands- und Überseeprogrammen der British Broadcasting Corporation (BBC) häufig zu hörenden sechs Sekundenimpulsen. Der Beginn des 6ten Impulses stellt die exakte Minute dar. Auf dem Übertragungsweg von Greenwich bis zum Sender der BBC treten Laufzeitverzögerungen auf, so daß die Signale der BBC hinter denen des Royal Greenwich Observatory ca. 0.1 s zurückbleiben.

The Royal Greenwich Observatory is the source of the "6-pips" time signals used by the British Broadcasting Corporation (BBC) in its domestic and overseas programmes. The signal is available for transmission every quarter-hour. The start of the long 6th "pip" marks the minute. The Royal Greenwich Observatory has no control over delays which may arise before transmission and the uncertainty of timing is therefore given as less than ± 0.1 s relative to UTC.

## Hawaii:

Radio Station WWVH, Department
of Commerce, National Bureau
of Standards, P.O.Box 417, Kekaha,
HI 96752

Stationen:

| WWVH | 2500 kHz | 5 kW |
| | 5000 kHz | 10 kW |
| | 10000 kHz | 10 kW |
| | 15000 kHz | 10 kW |

G. K.: 21° 59′ N, 159° 46′ W

Sendeschema:
siehe Beschreibung und Diagramm
unter Station WWV, USA

Bestätigung:
per QSL-Karte

## Hawaii:

Radio Station WWVH, Department
of Commerce, National Bureau
of Standards, P.O.Box 417, Kekaha,
HI 96752

Stations:

| WWVH | 2500 kHz | 5 kW |
| | 5000 kHz | 10 kW |
| | 10000 kHz | 10 kW |
| | 15000 kHz | 10 kW |

G. C.: 21° 59′ N, 159° 46′ W

Type of transmission:
see next diagram and descriptions
at station WWV (under USA).

V.
by QSL

## WWVH BROADCAST FORMAT

VIA TELEPHONE: (808) 335-4363 (NOT A TOLL-FREE NUMBE

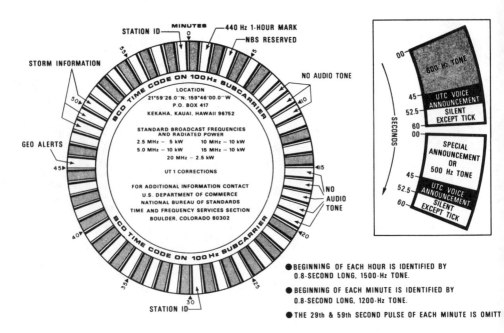

● BEGINNING OF EACH HOUR IS IDENTIFIED BY
0.8-SECOND LONG, 1500-Hz TONE.

● BEGINNING OF EACH MINUTE IS IDENTIFIED BY
0.8-SECOND LONG, 1200-Hz TONE.

● THE 29th & 59th SECOND PULSE OF EACH MINUTE IS OMITT

Department of Commerce

NATIONAL BUREAU OF STANDARDS

## RADIO STATION WWVH

KAUAI, HAWAII

2.5 MHz—21° 59' 31" N, 159° 46' 04" W    10.0 MHz—21° 59' 29" N, 159° 46' 02" W
5.0 MHz—21° 59' 21" N, 159° 45' 56" W    15.0 MHz—21° 59' 26" N, 159° 46' 00" W
20.0 MHz—21° 59' 24" N, 159° 45' 58" W

This is to confirm your reception report of WWVH

on ........ 10 ........ MHz.                      ........ Nov. 16, 1980 ........
      Frequencies                                              Date

Serial #    16,953          _____ C. L. Trendath _____
                                            Engineer-in-Charge

★ GPO 678-802

## Hong Kong:

Royal Observatory, Nathan Road,
Kowloon

Stationen:
VPS          500 kHz
   zu jeder geraden Stunde
VPS8         4232,5 kHz
   zu jeder ungeraden Stunde
   von 11.00 bis 21.00 UT
VPS35        8539 kHz
   zu jeder ungeraden Stunde
VPS6Ø        13020,5 kHz
   zu jeder ungeraden Stunde
   von 01.00 bis 15.00 UT
VPS8Ø        17096 kHz
   zu jeder ungeraden Stunde
   von 21.00 bis 13.00 UT
VPS22        22536 kHz
   zu jeder ungeraden Stunde
   von 01.00 bis 09.00 UT

Sendeschema:
Eine Serie von sechs Sekundenimpulsen. Der jeweils letzte Impuls stellt die
volle Stunde dar.

Station:
Royal Observatory Sender
95 MHz UKW

Sendezeiten:
alle 15 Minuten 24 Stunden täglich

Sendeschema:
Eine Serie von sechs Sekundenimpulsen.
Der Beginn des jeweils sechsten Impul-
ses stellt die volle Viertelstunde dar.

Station:
Hong Kong Aeradio
338, 6679, 8823, 13282 kHz

Sendezeiten:
um 15 und 45 Minuten nach jeder Stunde

Sendeschema:
Eine Serie von sechs Sekundenimpulsen.
Der Beginn des jeweils sechsten Impulses erfolgt um 15 bzw. 45 Minuten der
betreffenden Stunde.

## Hong Kong:

Royal Observatory, Nathan Road,
Kowloon

Stations:
VPS          500 kHz
   every even hour
VPS8         4232.5 kHz
   every odd hours
   from 11 to 21 UT
VPS35        8539 kHz
   every odd hour
VPS6Ø        13020.5 kHz
   every odd hours
   from 01 to 15 UT
VPS8Ø        17096 kHz
   every odd hours
   from 21 to 13 UT
VPS22        22536 kHz
   every odd hours
   from 01 to 09 UT

Type of transmission:
A series of 6 dots, the 6th dot being
on the hour

Station:
Royal Observatory Transmitter
95 MHz FM

Times:
every 15 minutes 24 hours daily

Type of transmission:
the 6th dot is on the hour, and on the
15th, 30th and 45th minute past each
hour.

Station:
Hong Kong Aeradio
338, 6679, 8823, 13282 kHz

Times:
at 15 and 45 minutes past every hour

Type of transmission:
Six dots at one second intervals, the
6th dot being the 15th and 45th minute
past the hour.

## Indien:

National Physical Laboratory,
Hillside Road, New Delhi-110012

Stationen:
ATA    5000 kHz  12.30-03.30 UTC
          10000 kHz  24.00
          15000 kHz  03.30-12.30 UTC

G. K.: $28^O$ 34' N, $77^O$ 19' Ost

Sendeleistung:
8 kW (PEP)

Sendeschema:
Die Sekundenimpulse haben eine Länge von 5 ms, die Minutenimpulse eine Länge von 100 ms. Die Impulse sind mit 1000 Hz moduliert. Während der Tonperioden erfolgt kurz vor und kurz nach den Impulsen eine kurze Unterbrechung der Tonaussendung. Während der ersten vier Minuten wird der Träger mit 1000 Hz moduliert. Während der nächsten elf Minuten wird der Träger durchgehend gesendet und mit den Sekunden- und Minutenimpulsen moduliert. Gegen Ende einer jeden Viertelstunde erfolgt eine Ansage in englischer Sprache.

Bestätigung:
QSL-Karte, Rückporto empfohlen

## India:

National Physical Laboratory,
Hillside Road, New Delhi-110012

Stations:
ATA    5000 kHz  12.30-03.30 UTC
          10000 kHz  24.00
          15000 kHz  03.30-12.30 UTC

G. C.: $28^O$ 34' N, $77^O$ 19' E

Power:
8 kW (PEP)

Type of transmission:
The seconds pulses consist of groups of 5 cycles of 1000 Hz. The minute pulses have a duration of 100 ms and are transmitted at the 60th seconds.
During the tone period, the seconds' and the minutes' pulses are transmitted preceded and followed by short interruptions of the modulated transmission. During the first four minutes, the carrier is transmitted modulated with 1000 Hz. During the next eleven minutes, the carrier is transmitted modulated with the seconds' pulses only. Voice announcements are towards the end of every 15 minutes.

V.
by QSL, Rp preferred

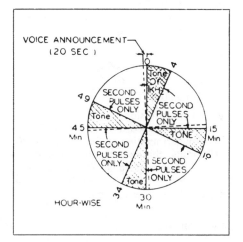

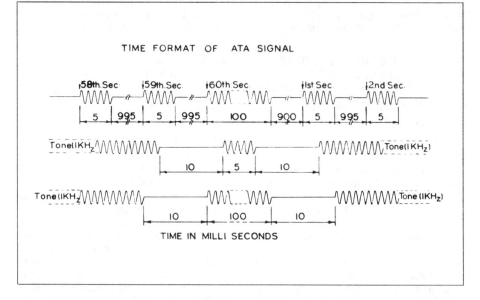

Bei den nachfolgenden Angaben über VWC handelt es sich um eine unbestätigte Meldung!

Kalkutta Radio VWC sendet Zeitsignale des Alipore Observatoriums, Kalkutta

Stationen:
VWC          434 kHz
             12745 kHz
Sendezeiten:
08.25-08.30 UTC
(Die Station wurde jedoch auch zu anderen Zeiten mit Zeitsendungen empfangen.)

Stationen:
VWC          434 kHz
             4286 kHz
Sendezeiten:
16.25-16.30 UTC

Sendeschema:
Zeitsignale entsprechend dem ONOGO-System endend um 08.30 bzw. 16.30 UTC täglich. Die Sendung beginnt mit „–.–.–" (Startsignal), „CQ CQ CQ DE VWC VWC VWC", gefolgt von den Sekunden- und Minutenimpulsen und „.–..." (Endsignal).

The following information about VWC are unconfirmed details!

Calcutta Radio VWC transmitting the time signals originating from the Alipore Observatory, Calcutta

Stations:
VWC          434 kHz
             12745 kHz
Times:
08.25-08.30 UTC
(Station also has been heard with time signals at other times.)

Stations:
VWC          434 kHz
             4286 kHz
Times:
16.25-16.30 UTC

Type of transmission:
Time signals according to the ONOGO-system, terminating at 08.30 and 16.30 UTC daily; these signals are preceded by „–.–.– (starting signal) CQ CQ CQ DE VWC VWC VWC – ordinary time signals – .–... (wait signal)"

V.
by letter, Rp

## Indonesien:

Directorate General of Posts and Telecommunications, Director of Operations, 37 Kebon Sirih Street, Jakarta

Stationen:
PKI    8542 kHz
PLC   11440 kHz

Sendezeiten:
00.55-01.00 UTC täglich

Sendeschema:
00.45-00.55 UTC:
CQ CQ CQ DE PKI/PLC
PKI/PLC PKI/PLC
    00 h 55 m 00 s — 00 h 56 m 50 s:
    1 Impuls pro Sekunde
    00 h 56 m 55 s — 00 h 57 m 00 s:
    5 Sekunden langer Ton
    00 h 57 m 05 s — 00 h 57 m 50 s:
    alle 10 Sekunden ein X —..—
    00 h 57 m 50 s — 00 h 58 m 00 s:
    1 Impuls pro Sekunde
    00 h 58 m 08 s — 00 h 58 m 50 s:
    alle 10 Sekunden ein N —.
    00 h 58 m 55 s — 00 h 59 m 00 s:
    1 Impuls pro Sekunde
    00 h 59 m 06 s — 00 h 59 m 50 s:
    alle 10 Sekunden ein G ——.
    00 h 59 m 55 s — 01 H 00 m 00 s:
    1 Impuls pro Sekunde

Bestätigung:
per Schreiben

Unbestätigte Information!

## Indonesia:

Directorate General of Posts and Telecommunications, Director of Operations, 37 Kebon Sirih Street, Jakarta

Stations:
PKI    8542 kHz
PLC   11440 kHz

Times:
00.55-01.00 UTC daily

Type of transmission:
00.45-00.55 UTC:
CQ CQ CQ DE PKI/PLC
PKI/PLC PKI/PLC
    00 h 55 m 00 s — 00 h 56 m 50 s:
    1dot at each second
    00 h 56 m 55 s — 00 h 57 m 00 s:
    5seconds' duration
    00 h 57 m 05 s — 00 h 57 m 50 s:
    a series of —..— (X) sent once
    every ten seconds
    00 h 57 m 50 s — 00 h 58 m 00 s:
    1 dot at each second
    00 h 58 m 08 s — 00 h 58 m 50 s:
    a series of 5 —. (N) sent
    once every ten seconds
    00 h 58 m 55 s — 00 h 59 m 50 s:
    1 dot at each second
    00 h 59 m 06 s — 00 h 59 m 50 s:
    a series of 5 ——. (G) sent
    once every ten seconds
    00 h 59 m 55 s — 01 h 00 m 00 s:
    1 dot at each second

V.:
by letter, Rp

Unconfirmed information!

# Italien:

Istituto Superiore delle Poste
e delle Telecomunicazioni, Ufficio $8^O$
Rep. $2^O$ – Viale Europa 190,
I-00144 Rom

Station:
IAM     5000 kHz

G. K.: $41^O$ 47' N, $12^O$ 27' Ost

Sendeleistung:
1 kW

Sendezeiten:
07.30-08.30 UTC
10.30-11.30 UTC wochentags
(während Sommerzeit eine Stunde
früher)

Sendeschema:
siehe Diagramm

Zeitangabe in langsamem Morsecode um
07.35, 07.50, 08.05, 08.20, 10.35,
10.50, 11.05 und 11.20 UTC.
Die Sekundenimpulse sind 5 ms lang mit
1000 Hz Modulation. Die Minutenimpulse sind auf 20 ms verlängert.

DUT 1:
CCIR code durch Impulsverdoppelung

Bestätigung:
per Schreiben

# Italy:

Istituto Superiore delle Poste
e delle Telecomunicazioni, Ufficio $8^O$
Rep. $2^O$ – Viale Europa 190,
I-00144-Rom

Station:
IAM     5000 kHz

G. C.: $41^O$ 47' N, $12^O$ 27' E

Power:
1 kW

Times:
07.30-08.30 UTC
10.30-11.30 UTC weekdays
(during daylight saving times one hour
earlier)

Type of transmission:
see the next diagram

Time is given in slow-speed Morse at
07.35, 07.50, 08.05, 08.20, 10.35,
10.50, 11.05 and 11.20 UTC.

The second pulse is made of 5 cycles of
a 1000 Hz standard frequency; the
minute pulse is made up of 20 cycles of
a 1000 Hz standard frequency.

DUT 1:
CCIR code by double pulse

V.
by letter, Rp

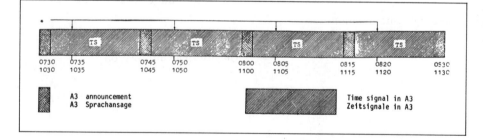

| | | | | | | | | |
|---|---|---|---|---|---|---|---|---|
| 0730 | 0735 | 0745 | 0750 | 0800 | 0805 | 0815 | 0820 | 0830 |
| 1030 | 1035 | 1045 | 1050 | 1100 | 1105 | 1115 | 1120 | 1130 |

A3  announcement
A3  Sprachansage

Time signal in A3
Zeitsignale in A3

Istituto Elettrotecnico Nazionale Galileo
Ferraris, Strada delle Cacce 91,
I-10135 Turin

Station:
IBF     5000 kHz

Istituto Elettrotechnico Nazionale Galileo
Ferraris, Strada delle Cacce 91,
I-10135 Torino

Station:
IBF     5000 kHz

| | |
|---|---|
| Sendestärke:<br>5 kW | Power:<br>5 kW |
| G. K.: 45$^{\circ}$ 02' N, 7$^{\circ}$ 42' Ost | G. C.: 45$^{\circ}$ 02' N, 7$^{\circ}$ 42' E |

Sendestärke:
5 kW

G. K.: 45$^{\circ}$ 02' N, 7$^{\circ}$ 42' Ost

Sendezeiten:
In den 15 Minuten vor 07.00, 09.00, 10.00, 11.00, 12.00, 13.00, 14.00, 15.00, 16.00, 17.00, 18.00 UTC. Während der Sommerzeit eine Stunde früher

Sendeschema:
siehe nachfolgendes Diagramm
Die Sekundenimpulse bestehen aus 5 Schwingungen eines 1000-Hz-Tones. Sieben solcher Impulse, jeweils mit 5-ms-Pausen, ergeben den Minutenimpuls. In den Minuten 50 und 00 wird das Rufzeichen (IBF) und die Zeitansage (MEZ) in CW gesendet. Zu Beginn und zum Ende jeder 15minütigen Sendung erfolgt in italienischer, französischer und englischer Sprache eine Stationskennung.

DUT 1:
CCIR-code durch Impulsverdoppelung

Bestätigung:
per QSL.

Power:
5 kW

G. C.: 45$^{\circ}$ 02' N, 7$^{\circ}$ 42' E

Times:
during the 15 minutes before 07.00, 09.00, 10.00, 11.00, 12.00, 13.00, 14.00, 15.00, 16.00, 17.00, 18.00 UTC. During daylight saving time one hour earlier.

Type of transmission:
as shown in the diagram
Each second marker is made of 5 cycles of a 1000 Hz tone, its beginning giving the time reference. Seven of the above mentioned pulses, with a 5 ms gap, mark the minute.
Call sign (IBF) and time announcements in CET at minutes 50 and 00 in CW.
At the beginning and the end of each 15 minutes transmission a voice announcement is transmitted in Italian, French and English language.

DUT 1:
CCIR-code by double pulse

V.
by QSL

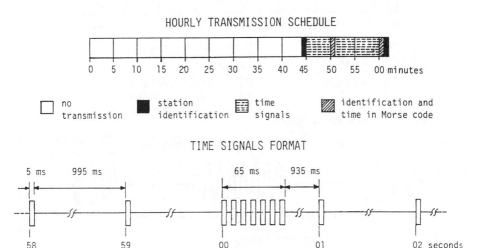

HOURLY TRANSMISSION SCHEDULE

0   5   10   15   20   25   30   35   40   45   50   55   00 minutes

□ no transmission    ■ station identification    ▦ time signals    ▨ identification and time in Morse code

TIME SIGNALS FORMAT

5 ms    995 ms        65 ms        935 ms

58        59        00        01        02 seconds

## Japan:

Frequency Standard Division,
The Radio Research Laboratory, Ministry
of Posts and Telecommunications,
Koganei 184, Tokio

Senderstandort:
  Sanwa, Ibaraki

G. K.: 36° 11' N, 139° 51' Ost

Stationen:
  JJY      2500 kHz
            5000 kHz
            8000 kHz
          10000 kHz
          15000 kHz

Sendeleistung: 2 kW

Sendezeiten:
24 Stunden täglich mit stündlichen Unterbrechungen zwischen der 35sten und 39sten Minute

Sendeschema:
Wie in den nachfolgenden Diagrammen dargestellt.

Bestätigung:
  per QSL-Karte

## Japan:

Frequency Standard Division,
The Radio Research Laboratory, Ministry
of Posts and Telecommunications,
Koganei 184, Tokio

Location:
  Sanwa, Ibaraki

G. C.: 36° 11' N, 139° 51' E

Stations:
  JJY      2500 kHz
            5000 kHz
            8000 kHz
          10000 kHz
          15000 kHz

Power:
  2 kW

Times:
24 hours daily, except interruptions between minutes 35 and 39 of each hour.

Type of transmission:
as shown in the following diagrams

V.:
  by QSL

### Hourly modulation schedule

### Wave form of second pulses

60

## Identification of minute signal by preceding marker

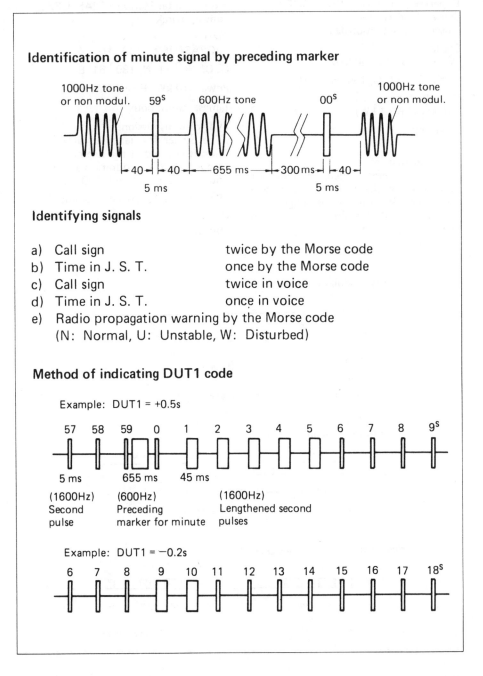

1000Hz tone
or non modul.    59ˢ    600Hz tone    00ˢ    1000Hz tone
or non modul.

├─40─┤├─40─┤├──655 ms──┤├─300 ms─┤├─40─┤
5 ms                                  5 ms

## Identifying signals

a)  Call sign                    twice by the Morse code
b)  Time in J. S. T.             once by the Morse code
c)  Call sign                    twice in voice
d)  Time in J. S. T.             once in voice
e)  Radio propagation warning by the Morse code
    (N:  Normal, U:  Unstable, W:  Disturbed)

## Method of indicating DUT1 code

Example:  DUT1 = +0.5s

57   58   59   0   1   2   3   4   5   6   7   8   9ˢ

5 ms        655 ms    45 ms

(1600Hz)    (600Hz)          (1600Hz)
Second      Preceding        Lengthened second
pulse       marker for minute pulses

Example:  DUT1 = −0.2s

6   7   8   9   10   11   12   13   14   15   16   17   18ˢ

## noch: Japan

Experimental Station JG2AS/JJF2,
Sanwa, Ibaraki
Anschrift wie Station JJY

Station:
  JG2AS/JJF2     40 kHz

G. K.: 36° 11′ N, 139° 51′ Ost

Sendeleistung:
  10 kW (ERP 1 kW)

Sendezeit:
  ständig

Sendeschema:
  Zu Beginn einer jeden Sekunde wird
  500 ms lang die Trägerfrequenz gesendet. Der 59ste Impuls hat lediglich eine
  Länge von 100 ms. Siehe auch nachfolgende Diagramme.

## Japan cont.

Experimental Station JG2AS/JJF2,
Sanwa, Ibaraki

Station:
  JG2AS/JJF2     40 kHz

G. C.: 36° 11′ N, 139° 51′ E

Power: 10 kW (ERP 1 kW)

Times: continuous

Type of transmission:
  The carrier frequency of 500 ms duration is emitted at the beginning of each
  second, but the duration of the 59th
  pulse in each minute is 100 ms.

  See also the following diagrams.
V.
  by QSL

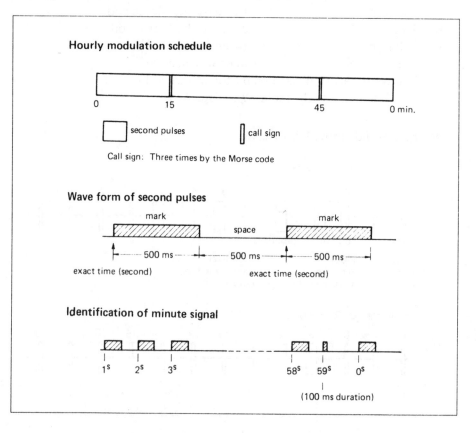

Hourly modulation schedule

0     15     45     0 min.

□ second pulses     ▮ call sign

Call sign: Three times by the Morse code

Wave form of second pulses

mark          space          mark

|← 500 ms →|← 500 ms →|← 500 ms →|

exact time (second)          exact time (second)

Identification of minute signal

1ˢ  2ˢ  3ˢ          58ˢ  59ˢ  0ˢ

(100 ms duration)

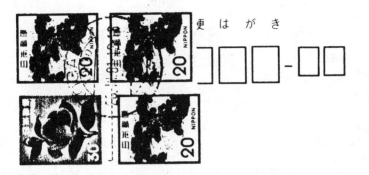

更 は が き

NIPPON 20
NIPPON 20
30
NIPPON 20

Mr. Gerd Klawitter
D-4430 Steinfurt
Ochtruper Str. 138
Fed. Rep. of Germany

Dear

報告ありがとうございました。

Thank you very much for your report. Your reception of

標準周波数および時刻信号の受信は

Standard Frequencies and Time Signals

| Carrier frequency | | Time of reception |
|---|---|---|
| 2500 kHz, | 5000 kHz | h  m  -  h  m(UTC) |
| 10000 kHz, | 15000 kHz | 26, Dec. 1980 (JST) |
| 8000 kHz | | |

確認されました。

has been verified by:

FREQUENCY STANDARD DIVISION
RADIO RESEARCH LABORATORIES
KOGANEI, TOKYO, 184, JAPAN

## Kanada:

Radio Station CHU, National Research Council of Canada, Ottawa, Ontario K1A OR6

Stationen:

| CHU | 3330 kHz | 3 kW |
|-----|----------|------|
|     | 7335 kHz | 10 kW |
|     | 14670 kHz | 3 kW |

G.K.: 45° 18' N, 75° 45' W

Modulation:
A3H

Sendezeiten:
24 Stunden täglich

Sendeschema:
Sekundenimpulse von 300 ms Länge mit 1000 Hz Ton. Der Beginn des Impulses ist die exakte Zeit. Der Minutenimpuls ist 500 ms lang, der Impuls zu jeder vollen Stunde sogar 1 Sekunde lang. Die Impulse werden im Abstand von einer Sekunde ausgestrahlt mit folgenden Ausnahmen:

1. Der 29ste Impuls jeder Minute fehlt.
2. Der 51ste bis einschließlich 59ste Impuls jeder Minute fehlen. Während dieser Zeit erfolgt die Stationskennung und Zeitansage in Sprache. In graden Minuten: „CHU Canada, Eastern Standard Time ... hours ... minutes ... heures ... minutes." In ungeraden Minuten: „CHU Canada, Heure Normale de l'Est ... heures ... minutes ... hours ... minutes."
3. In der ersten Minute jeder Stunde fehlen der erste bis einschließlich zehnte Sekundenimpuls.

CHU sendet in Digitalcode die Zeitangaben nach folgendem Schema:
1. Der NRC code verwendet das genormte kommerzielle 300 baud FSK System mit den Frequenzen 2025 und 2225 Hz entsprechend der Darstellung in der Abbildung. Der Code entspricht dem ASC2 (Fernschreibsystem), wobei alle 11 bit Zeichen 2 BCD Stellen enthalten. Die erste Ziffer ist die Zahl 6.

## Canada:

Radio Station CHU, National Research Council of Canada, Ottawa, Ontario K1A OR6

Stations:

| CHU | 3330 kHz | 3 kW |
|-----|----------|------|
|     | 7335 kHz | 10 kW |
|     | 14670 kHz | 3 kW |

G. C.: 45° 18' N, 75° 45' W

Modulation:
A3H

Times:
24 hours daily

Type of transmission:
Second pulses of 300 cycles of a 1000 Hz tone. The beginning of the pulse marks the exact second. The zero pulse of each minute is 0.5 second long, and the zero pulse of the hour is 1 second long. The pulse occur at the rate of one each second with the following exceptions:

1. The 29th pulse of each minute is omitted.
2. The 51st to 59th pulses inclusive of each minute are omitted, during this interval station identification and time is announced by voice.
3. The 1st to 10th pulses inclusive are omitted on the 1st minute of each hour.

A voice recording of the time occurs each minute in the ten second gap between the 50th and 60th second. It refers to the beginning of the minute or hour pulse that follows. The announcement is on the 24 hours system, alternating in French and English from minute to minute.

Voice announcements alternate in French and English: "CHU Canada, Eastern Standard Time ... hours ... minutes ... heures ... minutes" (even minutes); "CHU Canada, Heure Normale de l'Est ... heures ... minutes ... hours ... minutes" (odd minutes).

CHU is transmitting a digital time code in the following format:

Diese muß von der zu steuernden Uhr erkannt werden und schützt vor Code-Vertauschung. Mit den verbleibenden 9 Stellen werden Tag, Stunde, Minute und Sekunde dargestellt. Die gesamte Information wird anschließend wiederholt, und die ferngesteuerte Uhr läuft anschließend nur weiter, wenn die erste und die zweite Übermittlung der codierten Zeit sogar in Fällen fehlerfrei übermittelt werden, in denen das Verhältnis eines weißen Rauschens zum Nutzsignal noch 20 dB betrug. Bei noch größeren Störungen wurde zwar die Zeitübermittlung gestört, die zu steuernden Uhren erkennen jedoch die Störungen und laufen ungesteuert (nahezu präzis) weiter.

2. Die gesamte Information, einschließlich der Wiederholung, hat eine Länge von 0.365 Sekunden und kann daher in sechs Sekundenimpulsen „mit untergebracht" werden. Der Zeitcode wird minütlich von der 31sten bis zur 39sten Sekunde gesendet. Diese Sekundenimpulse, deren Beginn unverändert pünktlich erfolgt, beginnen mit einem Impuls von 10 ms Länge, danach folgt ein 125 ms langer Codeträger. Anschließend die 365 ms Zeitcode, so daß insgesamt seit dem Beginn der codierten Aussendung 0.5 Sekunden vergangen sind.

3. Das 11 bit Zeichen enthält einen Startbit, 2 Stopbits und 8 Datenbits aus 2 BCD-Stellen.

Bestätigung:
per QSL-Karte

1. The NRC code uses the standard commercial 300 baud FSK system, with frequencies of 2025 and 2225 Hz as shown in the figure. The code is modified ASCII in which each 11 bit character contains 2 BCD digits. The first digit is the number 6, which must be identified in the receiving clock and which protects against code inversion. The remaining 9 digits give the day, hour, minute and second. This message is repeated, and the remote clock will update at the end of the repeat message only if the two messages are identical in all respects. With this check feature error-free update has been obtained with broadband white noise 20 dB above the signal level. At higher noise levels the update is inhibited and finally suppressed, but no errors have been detected.

2. The total message, including the repeat, has a duration of 0.365 second and can therefore be incorporated into the seconds pulse. The time code is transmitted on the 31st to 39th seconds of each minute. The seconds pulse, which must remain "on time", starts with 10 periods, 0.01 s, of the normal 1 kHz signal. This is followed by 0.125 s of code carrier, and then 0.365 s of the code. The code ends, and update occurs, at 0.5 s, but the 0.5 s is added into the remote clock, along with the correct time zone hour, to bring the remote clock to the correct time.

3. The 11 bit character contains 1 start bit, 2 stop bits and 8 data bits of the 2 BCD digits.

V.
by QSL

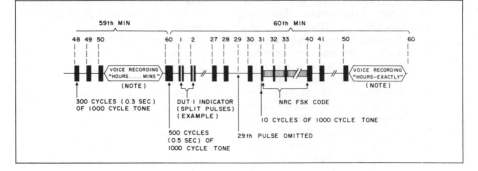

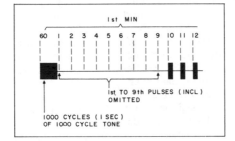

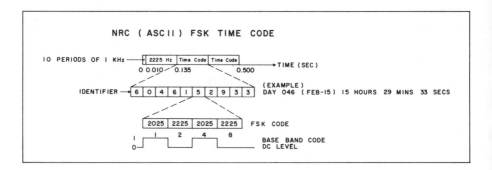

**CHU**
**CANADA**

SIR SANFORD FLEMING 1827-1915
Principal Advocate of    Principal promoteur des
Standard Time Zones   fuseaux horaires

## Korea (Rep.)

Korea Standards Research Institute,
P.O.Box 3, Taedok Science Town,
Taejon, Ch'ungnam 300-31

Station:
  HLA    5000 kHz

Sendeleistung:
  2 kW

G. K.: 36° 23' N, 127° 22' Ost

Sendezeit:
  Montags bis freitags (außer Feiertage)
  01.00-08.00 UTC

Sendeschema:
  Siehe Diagramme.
  Sekundenimpulse, die aus 9 Schwingungen einer 1800-Hz-Modulation bestehen. Der 29ste und 59ste Sekundenimpuls fehlen. Minutenimpuls: 500 ms lang mit 1800 Hz. Sprachansage (Stunden- und Minutendurchsage) nach dem 52sten Sekundenimpuls jeder Minute. BCD Time Code auf 100 Hz Unterträger (IRIG H).

DUT 1:
  CCIR-code durch Impulsverdoppelung

Bestätigung:
  per Brief

## Korea (Rep.)

Korea Standards Research Institute,
P.O.Box 3, Taedok Science Town,
Taejon, Ch'ungnam 300-31

Station:
  HLA    5000 kHz

Power:
  2 kW

G. C.: 36° 23' N, 127° 22' E

Times:
  mondays to fridays (except National holidays in Korea) 01.00-08.00 UTC

Type of transmission:
  Pulses of 9 cycles of 1800 Hz modulation. 29th and 59th second pulses are omitted. Hour identified by 500 ms long 1500 Hz tone. The beginning of each minute is identified by a 500 ms long 1800 Hz tone. Voice announcements of hours and minutes each minute following the 52nd second pulse BCD time code given on 100 Hz subcarrier (IRIG H).

DUT 1:
  CCIR code by double pulse.

V.
  by letter

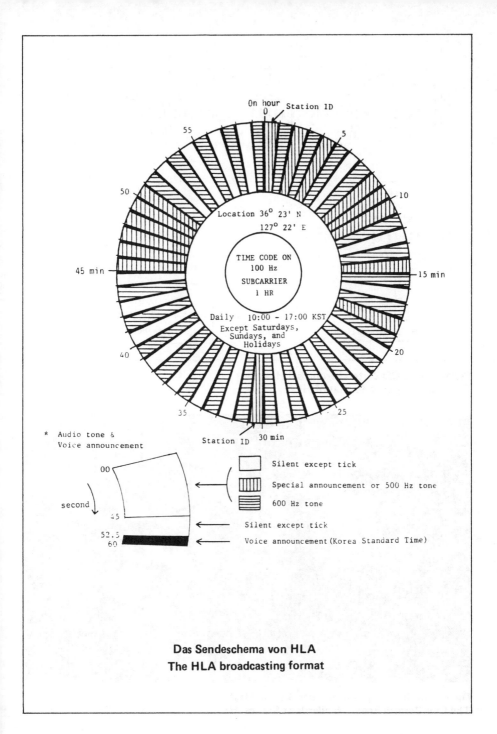

**Das Sendeschema von HLA**
**The HLA broadcasting format**

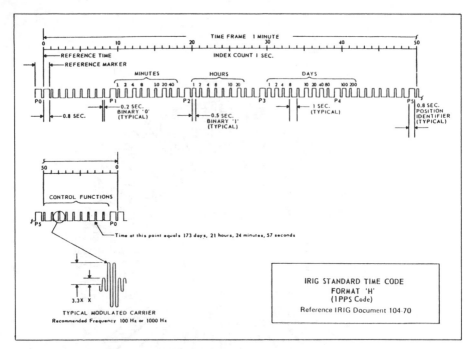

Schema der BCD Zeitcodierung bei HLA
The BCD time code format of HLA

Die vier Cäsiumstrahlnormale der Station HLA
The four Cesium Beam Standards of Station HLA

## Peru:

Centro de Comunicaciones Callao, Callao

Stationen:
OBC      485 kHz
         8650 kHz
         12307 kHz

Sendezeiten:
15.55-16.00 UTC
18.55-19.00 UTC
00.55-01.00 UTC

Sendeschema:
Modern American Modified System.
Sekundenimpulse von 100 ms Länge,
Stundenimpuls von 1 Sekunde Länge.

Bestätigung:
per Schreiben

Unbestätigte Informationen!

## Peru:

Centro de Comunicaciones Callao, Callao

Stations:
OBC      485 kHz
         8650 kHz
         12307 kHz

Times:
15.55-16.00 UTC
18.55-19.00 UTC
00.55-01.00 UTC

Type of transmission:
The time signals begin at 00.55, 15.55
and 18.55 UTC. During the five minutes
of transmission, each beat of the clock
is transmitted in the form shown in
the diagram "Modern American Modified System". A beat lasts 100 ms. The
last signal begins at the 59th second
of the 5th minute (lasting 1 sec) and its
end indicates the exact time.

V.
by letter, Rp

Unconfirmed information!

## Philippinen:

Commanding Officer, US Naval
Communication Station,
FPO San Francisco, CA 96656, USA

Stationen:
NPO     4445   kHz
        10440,5 kHz
        12804   kHz

Sendezeiten:
05.55-06.00, 11.55-12.00,
17.55-18.00, 23.55-24.00 UTC

Sendeschema:
CW Sekundenimpulse

## Philipines:

Commanding Officer, US Naval
Communication Station,
FPO San Francisco, CA 96656, USA

Stations:
NPO     4445   kHz
        10440,5 kHz
        12804   kHz

Times:
05.55-06.00, 11.55-12.00,
17.55-18.00, 23.55-24.00 UTC

Type of transmission:
CW seconds pulses

## Spanien:

Instituto y Observatorio de Marina,
San Fernando (Cádiz)

Stationen:
EBC    6840 kHz   10.29-10.55 UTC
       12008 kHz   09.59-10.25 UTC

G. K.: $36^o$ 28' N, $6^o$ 12' W

Modulation:
A3H

Sendeschema:
09.59-10.00 UTC
   CQ CQ CQ DE EBC EBC EBC
   HORA HORA HORA in langsamem
   Morsecode (A2)
10.00-10.25 UTC
   Zeitimpulse von 100 ms Länge und
   1000 Hz Modulation. Minutenimpulse 500 ms/1250 Hz (A2)
Die Sendung um 10.29 UTC auf 6840
kHz erfolgt in der gleichen Weise.

DUT1:
CCIR-Code durch Impulsverdoppelung

Bestätigung:
per Schreiben


Die Frequenz 12008 kHz wird in Kürze
durch 11173.5 kHz ersetzt werden.

## Spain:

Instituto y Observatorio de Marina,
San Fernando (Cádiz)

Stations:
EBC    6840 kHz   10.29-10.55 UTC
       12008 kHz   09.59-10.25 UTC

G. C.: $36^o$ 28' N, $6^o$ 12' W

Modulation:
A3H

Type of transmission:
09.59-10.00 UTC
   CQ CQ CQ DE EBC EBC EBC
   HORA HORA HORA in slow
   Morse (A2)
10.00-10.25 UTC
   Time Signals of 100 ms length
   (1000 Hz). At each complete
   minute a signal of 500 ms length
   (1250 Hz). (A2)
The transmission on 6840 kHz at 10.29
UTC is built up in the same manner.

DUT1:
CCIR code by double pulse

V.
by letter, Rp


The frequency 12008 kHz is to be replaced by 11173.5 kHz in the near future.

## Sri Lanka:

Colombo Radio 4PB, Coastal Radio
Station, Colombo 8

Stationen:

| 4 PB | 482 kHz | Modulation A2 |
|------|---------|---------------|
|      | 8473 kHz | Modulation A1 |

Sendezeiten:
05.53-06.00, 13.23-13.30 UTC

Sendeschema:
Zeitsignale vom Colombo Observatorium
wie nachfolgend:

53 m 00 s − 55 m 00 s
   C CQ CQ DE 4PB 4 PB QSW
   482/8473 KHZ TIME SIGNALS,
   WEATHER REPORT, FLEET
   FORECAST, NAV WNG AND TFC
   LIST UP AS in langsamem Morse-
   code, gefolgt von ,,.−...''
55 m 00 s − 60 m 00 s
   Sekundenimpulse von 100 ms Län-
   ge, Minutenimpulse von 400 ms
   Länge

Bestätigung:
per Schreiben

Unbestätigte Information!

## Sri Lanka:

Colombo Radio 4PB, Coastal Radio
Station, Colombo 8

Stations:

| 4 PB | 482 kHz | Modulation A2 |
|------|---------|---------------|
|      | 8473 kHz | Modulation A1 |

Times:
05.53-06.00, 13.23-13.30 UTC

Type of transmission:
The time signals originate from the
Colombo Observatory, and the trans-
mission takes place as follows:

53 m 00 s − 55 m 00 s
   C CQ CQ DE 4PB 4 PB QSW
   482/8473 KHZ TIME SIGNALS,
   WEATHER REPORT, FLEET
   FORECAST, NAV WNG AND TFC
   LIST UP AS in slow Morse followed
   by ''.−...''
55 m 00 s − 60 m 00 s
   A series of 100 ms dots at each
   second. The minute dots are 400
   ms long to facilitate identification.
   The beginning of each dot is the
   time reference point.

V.
by letter, Rp


Unconfirmed information!

## Südafrika:

National Physical Laboratory,
P.O.Box 395, Pretoria 0001

Stationen:
| ZUO | 2500 kHz | 4 kW |
|-----|----------|------|
|     | 5000 kHz | 4 kW |
|     | 100 MHz  | 80 Watt |

G. K.: 25° 58' S, 28° 14' Ost

Sendezeiten:
18.00-04.00 UTC auf 2500 kHz
ständig auf 5000 kHz und 100 MHz

Sendeschema:
Die Kurzwellensender sind amplituden-moduliert, der UKW-Sender ist phasen-moduliert. Die Sekundenimpulse sind 5 ms lang mit 1000 Hz moduliert. Der Minutenimpuls hat eine Länge von 500 ms.
In der allen vollen fünf Minuten vorangehenden Minute erfolgt eine morse-codierte Ansage mit 600 Hz Modulation: Dreimal das Rufzeichen sowie die Zeit der folgenden Minute. Die betreffende nachfolgende Minute wird durch den Beginn des nächsten Impulses dargestellt. Auf 2500 kHz und 5000 kHz werden beide AM-Seitenbänder ausgestrahlt.

DUT1:
CCIR-Code durch Impulsverdoppelung.

Bestätigung:
per Schreiben oder QSL-Karte

## South Africa:

National Physical Laboratory,
P.O.Box 395, Pretoria 0001

Stations:
| ZUO | 2500 kHz | 4 kW |
|-----|----------|------|
|     | 5000 kHz | 4 kW |
|     | 100 MHz  | 80 Watts |

G. C.: 25° 58' S, 28° 14' E

Times:
18.00-04.00 UTC auf 2500 kHz
continuous on 5000 kHz and 100 MHz

Type of transmission:
The 2500 kHz and 5000 kHz transmitters are amplitude modulated. The 100 MHz transmitter is phase modulated. The signals consist of one pulse per second, each pulse consisting of 5 cycles of 1000 Hz tone. The first pulse in every minute is lengthened to 500 ms.
Morse announcements are made during the minute preceding every 5th minute. They consist of the call sign (ZUO) repeated three times and the Universal Time at the next minute. The correct time is indicated by the beginning of a time pulse. On the 2.5 and 5 MHz transmissions double side band modulation is employed. Modulation of the first half cycles of each pulse is positive. The audio frequency of the time pulses is 1000 Hz, that one of the morse announcements is 600 Hz.

DUT1:
CCIR code by double pulses

V.
by QSL or letter

## noch: Südafrika

Cape Town Radio, Private Bag X-1,
Milnerton 7435

Stationen:
| ZSC | 418 kHz | 5 kW |
| | 4291 kHz | 10 kW |
| | 8461 kHz | 10 kW |
| | 12724 kHz | 10 kW |
| | 17018 kHz | 10 kW |
| | 22455 kHz | 10 kW |

Sendezeiten:
07.55-08.00, 16.55-17.00 UTC

Sendeschema:
Unmodulierte Sekundenimpulse von 100 ms Länge. Die unmodulierten Minutenimpulse sind 400 ms lang. Um die Station identifizieren zu können, müßten die den Zeitzeichensendungen vorangehenden traffic-lists um 06.30 und 16.30 UTC gehört werden.

Bestätigung:
per QSL

## South Africa cont.

Cape Town Radio, Private Bag X-1,
Milnerton 7435

Stations:
| ZSC | 418 kHz | 5 kW |
| | 4291 kHz | 10 kW |
| | 8461 kHz | 10 kW |
| | 12724 kHz | 10 kW |
| | 17018 kHz | 10 kW |
| | 22455 kHz | 10 kW |

Times:
07.55-08.00, 16.55-17.00 UTC

Type of transmission:
A1 CW approximately 100 ms carrier, 900 ms silence, — each second, with the 60th second 400 ms carrier, 600 ms silence. There is no other identification other than the traffic list at 06.30 and 16.30 UTC.

V.
by QSL, no Rp required

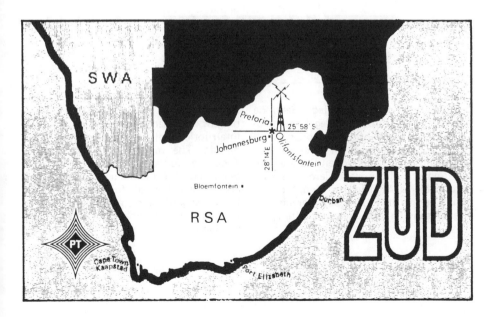

## Schweiz:

Observatoire de Neuchâtel, Rue de l'Observatoire 58, CH-2000 Neuchâtel

Station:
HBG   75 kHz
(Der Sender wird von der Radio Schweiz AG, Bern, betrieben)

G. K.: 46° 24' N, 6° 15' Ost

Sendeleistung:
20 kW

Sendezeit:
ständig

Sendeschema:
wie im nachfolgenden Diagramm dargestellt

## Switzerland:

Observatoire de Neuchâtel, Rue de l'Observatoire 58, CH-2000 Neuchâtel

Station:
HBG   75 kHz
(transmitter operated by Radio Swisse AG, Berne)

G. C.: 46° 24' N, 6° 15' E

Power:
20 kW

Times:
continuous

Type of transmission:
as shown in the diagram

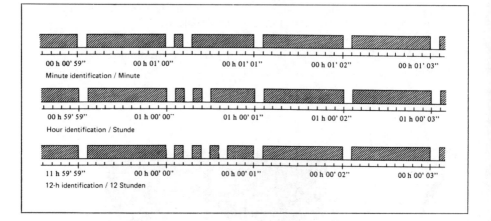

Der Träger wird zu Beginn jeder Sekunde für 100 ms unterbrochen (Negativmodulation). Zu Beginn einer jeden vollen Minute wird der Träger zweimal unterbrochen, zu Beginn einer jeden vollen Stunde dreimal und um Mitternacht viermal. Besondere codierte Signale zur Kenntlichmachung der Normal- bzw. Sommerzeit sind ebenfalls in den Sendungen enthalten.

Interruption of the carrier at the beginning of every second for 100 ms. Another interruption follows the signal for the minute. The minutes are identified by a double pulse, the hours by a triple pulse and the midnight by four pulses. Special coded signals for updating clocks from standard time to summer time vice versa are included at certain times of the emission.

## Taiwan:

Telecommunication Laboratories,
Ministry of Communications,
P.O.Box 71, Chung-Li, Taiwan 32099,
Republik China

Stationen:
BSF      5000 kHz
         15000 kHz

G. K.: $24^O$ 57' N, $121^O$ 9' Ost

Sendeleistung:
2 kW

Sendezeiten:
ständig

Sendeschema:
Sekundenimpulse von 5 ms Länge mit 1000 Hz Modulation zwischen den Minuten 00-05, 10-15, 20-25, 30-35, 40-45 und 50-55. Sekundenimpulse von 5 ms Länge unmoduliert zwischen den Minuten 05-10, 15-20, 25-30, 45-50 und 55-60. Die Minutenimpulse sind 300 ms lang. In der 9ten, 19ten, 29ten, 49sten und 59sten Minute wird eine Ansage in Morsecode und in chinesischer Sprache gesendet. Nähere Einzelheiten siehe nachfolgendes Diagramm.

DUT1:
CCIR-Code durch Impulsverlängerung.

Bestätigung:
per QSL-Karte

## Taiwan:

Telecommunication Laboratories,
Ministry of Communications,
P.O.Box 71, Chung-Li, Taiwan 32099,
Republik China

Stations:
BSF      5000 kHz
         15000 kHz

G. C.: $24^O$ 57' N, $121^O$ 9' E

Power:
2 kW

Times:
continuous

Type of transmission:
Second pulses of 5 ms duration with 1000 Hz modulation between the minutes 00-05, 10-15, 20-25, 30-35, 40-45 and 50-55. Second pulses of 5 ms duration without modulation between the minutes 05-10, 15-20, 25-30, 45-50 and 55-60. The minute marker is a pulse of 300 ms duration. During the 9th, 19th, 29th, 49th, and 59th minute, Morse Code and Chinese voice announcement of time.

See also the following diagrams.

DUT1:
CCIR code by pulse lengthening.

V.
by QSL, Rp

Daily transmission schedule

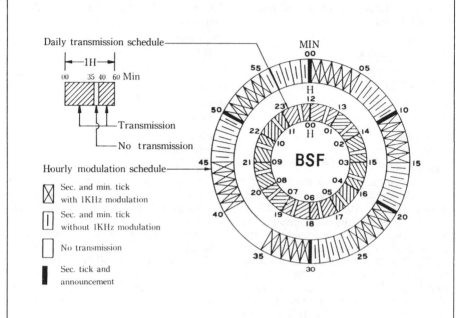

Hourly modulation schedule

☒ Sec. and min. tick
  with 1KHz modulation

▯ Sec. and min. tick
  without 1KHz modulation

▢ No transmission

▮ Sec. tick and
  announcement

Second tick

(1)Second pulses of 5 ms duration, without 1 KHz modulation

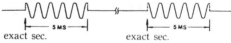

(2)Second pulses of 5 ms duration with 1KHz modulation

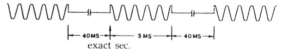

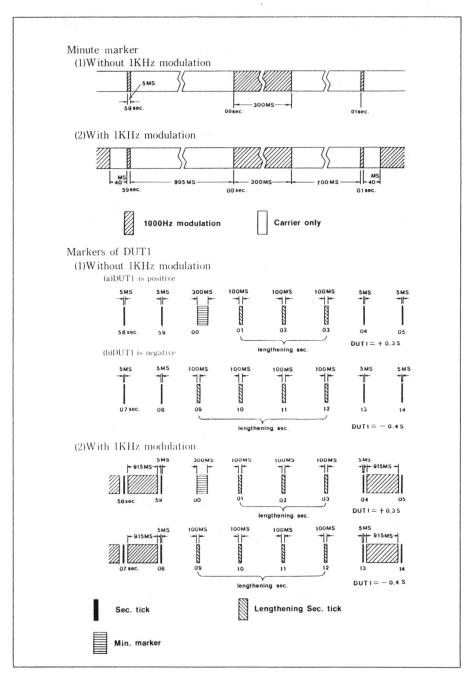

## Tschechoslowakei:

Astronomical Institute, Budecská 6, 12023 Prag 2

Station:
OMA 50 (Standort Liblice)

G. K.: $50^\circ 4'$ N, $14^\circ 53'$ Ost

Frequenz:
50 kHz

Sendeleistung: 7 kW

Sendezeiten:
Ständig mit Wartungsunterbrechungen an jedem ersten Mittwoch des Monats von 06.00 bis 12.00 UT. Während dieser Zeit ist ein Ersatzsender mit schwächerer Sendeleistung in Podebrady in Betrieb.

Sendeschema:
Der Träger ist amplituden- und phasengesteuert. Es handelt sich um negative Amplitudenmodulation, d. h. daß der Träger während der Sekundenimpulse für 100 ms unterbrochen wird. Die Minutenimpulse sind 500 ms lang. Die exakte Zeit liegt zu Beginn der Unterbrechung vor. Minütlich wird die Zeit in codierter Form gesendet. Die Tageszeit wird in Phasenumkehr des Trägers bestimmter Sekundenimpulse gesendet, und zwar zwischen 200 ms und 300 ms einiger Impulse. In jeder Minute werden 4 Phasenimpulse (P1 bis P4) gesendet. Zusammen mit den amplitudengesteuerten Minutenimpulsen (M) werden 4 Zeitintervalle gebildet, die — gemessen in Sekunden — vier Dinge darstellen: die Einerstellen der Minuten (UM), die Zehnerstellen der Minuten (TM), die Einerstellen der Stunden (UH) und die Zehnerstellen der Stunden (TH). Wie im Diagramm ersichtlich, wird die Dauer jeden Intervalls auf 1 Sekunde verlängert, so daß die Ziffer Null wie ein sekündliches Intervall gesendet werden kann. Um zwischen tschechoslowakischer Normal- und Sommerzeit unterscheiden zu können, wird das TH-Intervall im Fall der Sommerzeit um 4 Sekunden verlängert.

## Czechoslovakia:

Astronomical Institute, Budecská 6, 12023 Prag 2

Station:
OMA 50 (Position Liblice)

G. C.: $50^\circ 4'$ N, $14^\circ 53'$ E

Frequency:
50 kHz

Power:
7 kW

Times:
continuous; scheduled maintenance interruption on each first Wednesday of every month from 0600 h to 1200 h UT. For OMA 50 an auxiliary transmitter in Podebrady with reduced power is used during these intervals.

Type of transmission:
The carrier is both amplitude and phase keyed. The amplitude keying is negative, i.e. the carrier is being interrupted during the 100 ms seconds ticks. At full minute the duration of the tick is 500 ms. The precise time is given by the beginning of the interruption. A time code transmission is effected every minute. The time of day is transmitted by means of carrier phase reversals from 200 to 300 ms during certain seconds of the respective minute. Thus, in each minute a series of 4 phase-pulses (P1 to P4) is transmitted. These phase-pulses together with the amplitude minute pulse (M) form 4 time intervals which, measured in seconds, represent four numbers: units of minutes (UM), tens of minutes (TM), units of hours (UH), and tens of hours (TH) of the UT time scale. As shown in the diagram of Time Code Format transmitted by OMA 50 the duration of each interval is prolongated by 1 sec so that the number 0 may be transmitted as an one second interval. To distinguisch between the standard and summer time in Czechoslovakia the interval corresponding to tens of hours in the latter case is extended by supplementary 4 seconds. This allows for

Eine Kalenderinformation (Tag der Woche, Monat und Tag des Monats) wird während vier weiterer Phasenumkehrintervalle gesendet. Dieses geschieht in bestimmten Sekunden zwischen 300 und 400 ms. Diese vier Phasenimpulse werden mit D1 bis D4 gekennzeichnet und bilden zusammen mit dem A1-Minutenimpuls (M) vier Zeitintervalle. Sie stellen — gemessen in Sekunden — vier Ziffern dar: Tag der Woche (1 für Montag), Einer und Zehner des Monatstages und Ziffer des Monats.

Siehe hierzu auch das im Diagramm dargestellte Beispiel. Stationsrufzeichen und DUT1-Code werden nicht gesendet. Nähere Informationen sind erhältlich von „Institute of Radioengineering and Electronics, cp. 1014, 182 51 Prag 5 — Kobylisy.

a compatible and simple option of either kind of time at the decoding level.

A calendar information about the day of week, month and day of month is also transmitted through another 4 phase reversals in the interval from 300 to 400 ms of the corresponding second. Thus similarly the 4 phase-pulses (D1 to D4) with the A1 minute pulse (M) form 4 time intervals which measured in seconds represent four numbers: day of week (1 for Monday, units and tens of the day of month and number of month. A one second interval is added to those of units and tens of the day of month. A one second interval is added to those of units and tens of the day of month to enable the transmission of zero as a just one second interval. Station call sign and DUT1 code are not transmitted.

Further information can be received from: Institut of Radioengineering and Elektronics, cp. 1014, 182 51 Prague 8 — Kobylisy.

**Darstellung des Zeitcodes von OMA 50 kHz**
**Chart of Time Code transmissions from OMA-50 kHz**

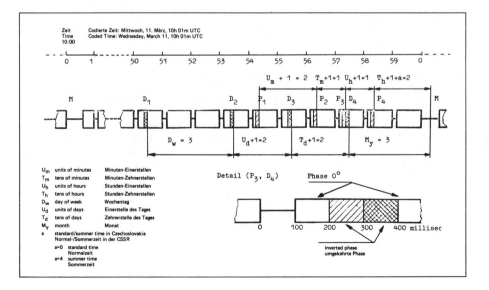

## noch: Tschechoslowakei

## Czechoslovakia cont.

Station:
OMA 2500    (Standort Liblice)

Station:
OMA 2500    (Position Liblice)

Frequenz:
2500 kHz

Frequency:
2500 kHz

Sendeleistung:
1 kW

Power:
1 kW

Sendezeiten:
durchgehend; Wartungsunterbrechungen
an jedem ersten Mittwoch des Monats
von 06.00 bis 12.00 UT

Times:
continuous; scheduled maintenance interruption on each first Wednesday of
every month from 0600 h to 1200 h UT.

Sendeschema:
Sekundenimpulse von 100 ms Länge,
Minutenimpulse von 500 ms Länge
(Ersatzprogramm ohne Rufzeichen).

Type of transmission:
Time pulses of 100 ms for the seconds
and 500 ms for the minutes. (Emer-
gency program without callsign)

Station:
OLB5    (Standort Liblice)

Station:
OLB5    (Position Liblice)

Frequenz:
3170 kHz

Frequency
3170 kHz

Sendeleistung:
5 kW

Power:
5 kW

Sendezeiten:
durchgehend; Wartungsunterbrechungen
an jedem ersten Mittwoch des Monats
von 06.00 bis 12.00 UT

Times:
continuous; scheduled maintenance interruption on each first Wednesday of
every month from 0600 h to 1200 h UT

Sendeschema:
Sekundenimpulse von 100 ms Länge
und Minutenimpulse von 500 ms Länge.
Bis auf die Ausnahme der positiven
Amplitudenmodulation wird der Sender
genau wie der Sender OMA50 gesteuert,
da beide Stationen von der gleichen
Uhr angesteuert werden. Stationsrufzeichen und DUT1-Code werden nicht
gesendet.

Type of transmission:
The carrier is keyed by the time signals
of 100 ms every second and of 500 ms
every minute. The transmitter keying is,
except for being positive, identical with
keying of the transmitter OMA 50 in
Liblice, as it originates from the same
clock there.
Station call sign and DUT1 code are not
transmitted. Relocation of the OLB5
transmission to Liblice is considered
for the near future.

Bestätigung:
per QSL-Karte

V.
by QSL

# OMA CZECHOSLOVAKIA

**USA:**

Commanding Officer, US Naval Communication Station (NPG), Stockton, CA 95203

Frequenzen:
   3268  kHz
   6428,5 kHz
   9277,5 kHz
   12966  kHz

Sendezeiten:
00.55-01.00, 02.55-03.00, 06.55-07.00, 21.55-22.00 UTC zu unregelmäßigen Zeiten

Bestätigung:
   per QSL-Karte

**USA:**

Commanding Officer, US Naval Communication Station (NPG), Stockton, CA 95203

Frequencies:
   3268  kHz
   6428,5 kHz
   9277,5 kHz
   12966  kHz

Times:
00.55-01.00, 02.55-03.00, 06.55-07.00, 21.55-22.00 UTC on irregular dates

V.
   by QSL, Rp

UNITED STATES NAVAL COMMUNICATIONS STATION
SAN FRANCISCO

QSL QSO
TO ARS: MR KLAWITTER

EMISSION: CW (A1)

DATE: 31 AUG 72

TIME: 0630 GMT

NPG XMIT: 13655 KHZ

NPG RCV: NA

REMARKS: TRANSMITTER FOR

THIS FREQ IS LOCATED IN HAWAII (NPM)

TYPE OF MITTER USED UNKNOWN.

73'S

SIGNATURE M F WARE RMC M.F.Ware

Radio Station WWV, 2000 East County Road 58, Fort Collins, Colorado 80524

Stationen:

| | |
|---|---|
| 2500 kHz | 2.5 kW |
| 5000 kHz | 10 kW |
| 10000 kHz | 10 kW |
| 15000 kHz | 10 kW |
| 20000 kHz | 2.5 kW |

G. K.: 40° 41′ N, 105° 2′ W

Sendezeiten:
ständig

Sendeschema:
Es findet ein 0 bis 24 Stundensystem Anwendung mit Beginn um 0000 UTC. Es erfolgen Zeitansagen, wobei sich die in der Ansage genannte Zeit auf den Moment bezieht, zu dem der 800 ms lange Ton beginnt. Bei WWV wird in den letzten 7.5 Sekunden jeder Minute die Zeit angesagt. Um 10.35 UTC lautet sie beispielsweise: „At the tone, ten hours, thirty-five minutes Coordinated Universal Time". Bei WWVH erfolgt diese Zeitansage zwischen der 45sten und 52.5ten Sekunde jeder Minute. Wer also sowohl WWV als auch gleichzeitig WWVH empfängt, hört zunächst die Ansage von WWVH und nach einer Pause von 7.5 Sekunden die gleiche Ansage von WWV. Der nach beiden Ansagen folgende Ton verläßt beide Sender absolut zeitgleich, erreicht den Empfänger wegen unterschiedlicher Signallaufzeiten jedoch zu geringfügig unterschiedlichen Zeiten.
WWV und WWVH senden Amplitudenmodulation mit beiden Seitenbändern. Der Modulationsgrad beträgt:
25 % beim IRIG-H-Code
50 % beim 600-Hz-Ton
75 % bei Sprachsendungen
100 % bei den Sekundenimpulsen.

DUT1:
CCIR-Code durch Impulsverdoppelung und BCD-Zeitcodierung auf 100-Hz-Unterträger.

Bestätigung:
per QSL-Karte

Radio Station WWV, 2000 East County Road 58, Fort Collins, Colorado 80524

Stations:

| | |
|---|---|
| 2500 kHz | 2.5 kW |
| 5000 kHz | 10 kW |
| 10000 kHz | 10 kW |
| 15000 kHz | 10 kW |
| 20000 kHz | 2.5 kW |

G.C.: 40° 41′ N, 105° 2′ W

Times:
continuous

Types of transmission:
as shown in the diagram

The 0 to 24 hour system is used starting with 0000 UTC. The time announcement refers to the end of an announcement interval, i.e., to the time when the 800 ms long audio tone begins. At WWV a voice announcement of UTC is given during the last 7.5 seconds of every minute. At 10.35 UTC, for instance, the voice announcement (given in English) is: "At the tone, ten hours, thirty-five minutes Coordinated Universal Time." At WWVH a voice announcement occurs during the period 45 seconds to 52.5 seconds after the minute. It should be noted that the voice announcement for WWVH precedes that of WWV by 7.5 seconds. However, the tone markers referred to in both announcements occur simultaneously, though they may not be so received due to propagation effects.
At WWV and WWVH, double sideband amplitude modulation is employed with 50 percent modulation on the steady tones, 25 percent for IRIG-H code, 100 percent for second pulses, and 75 percent for voice.

DUT1:
CCIR code by double pulse. BCD time code given on the 100 Hz subcarrier, includes DUT1 correction.

V.
by QSL

## WWV BROADCAST FORMAT

VIA TELEPHONE: (303) 499-7111
(NOT A TOLL-FREE NUMBER)

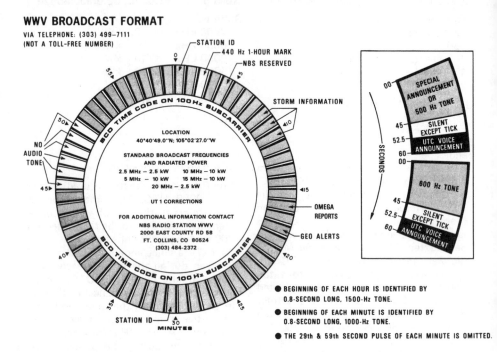

- BEGINNING OF EACH HOUR IS IDENTIFIED BY 0.8-SECOND LONG, 1500-Hz TONE.
- BEGINNING OF EACH MINUTE IS IDENTIFIED BY 0.8-SECOND LONG, 1000-Hz TONE.
- THE 29th & 59th SECOND PULSE OF EACH MINUTE IS OMITTED.

Radio Station WWVB, 2000 East County Road 58, Fort Collins, Colorado 80524

Station:
  WWVB          60 kHz

G. K.: $40^o$ 40' N, $105^o$ 3' W

Sendeleistung:
  10 kW

Sendezeit:
  ständig

Sendeschema:
  Sekundenimpulse durch Reduzierung der Trägeramplitude (Negativmodulation). Es erfolgt eine Übertragung des Datums, der Zeit und des DUT1-Wertes in BCD-Code.

Bestätigung:
  per QSL-Karte

Radio Station WWVB, 2000 East County Road 58, Fort Collins, Colorado 80524

Station:
  WWVB          60 kHz

G. C.: $40^o$ 40' N, $105^o$ 3' W

Power:
  10 kW

Times:
  continuous

Type of transmission:
  Second pulses given by reduction of the amplitude of the carrier. BCD-coded announcement of the date and time and of the correction to obtain UT1. No CCIR code.

V.
  by QSL

## Radio Station WWV
## via GOES-Satelliten

## Radio Station WWV
## via GOES-satellites

Zusätzlich zu den Zeitzeichenaussendungen der Stationen WWV/WWVB und WWVH beteiligt sich das National Bureau of Standards (NBS) an den Zeitzeichenaussendungen der drei GOES-Satelliten (GOES = Geostationary Operational Environmental Satellite), die der National Oceanic and Atmospheric Administration (NOAA) gehören.

Drei GOES-Satelliten befinden sich zur Zeit auf einem geostationären Orbit, zwei davon sind in Betrieb, ein weiterer dient Reservezwecken. Der westliche Satellit arbeitet auf 468,825 MHz und befindet sich auf 135° westlicher Länge über dem Äquator. Der östliche Satellit kann auf 468,8375 MHz empfangen werden, er befindet sich auf 75° westlicher Länge. Der Reservesatellit befindet sich zur Zeit auf 105° westlicher Länge über dem Äquator.

Die Zeitzeichenaussendung ist nur einer von mehreren Anwendungsbereichen von GOES. Die empfangenen Sendungen enthalten überwiegend nicht zeitzeichenbezogene Daten nach folgendem Schema: Zunächst beginnt die Übertragun der codierten Zeit (TC = Time Code) von 30 Sekunden Dauer, danach folgt eine sog. Interrogation Message, auf die hier nicht näher eingegangen werden soll, da sie bezüglich der Zeitübertragung ohne Bedeutung ist.

Die TC-Übertragung startet mit einer Synchronisation, gefolgt von der eigentlichen Zeitübertragung (Time of year), bestehend aus Tag des Jahres, Stunde, Minute und Sekunde. Anschließend wird der DUT1-Wert sowie Daten über die gegenwärtige Position und die präzise Höhe des Satelliten über der Erdoberfläche übertragen.

As a complement to its other time and frequency services, NBS is sponsoring a satellite-disseminated time code using the GOES (Geostationary Operational Environmental Satellite) satellites of the National Oceanic and Atmospheric Administration (NOAA). The time code is referenced to the NBS time scale and gives Coordinated Universal Time (UTC). Although the time code was designed to provide a means of dating environmental data collected by the GOES satellites, it can also be used as a general-purpose time reference for many other applications. The time code is available to the entire Western Hemisphere from two satellites on a near full-time basis.

There are three GOES satellites in orbit, two in operational status with a third serving as an in-orbit spare. The western satellite operates at 468.825 MHz and is located at 135° West Longitude. The eastern satellite is received on 468.8375 MHz and is positioned at 75° West Longitude. The spare is at 105° West Longitude. Coverages of the two operational satellites are shown in the figure.

The GOES satellites collect environmental data from remote sensors. The time code is part of the interrogation channel which is used to communicate with these sensors. The interrogation messages an time code are prepared and sent to the GOES satellites from Wallops Island, Virginia. NBS maintains atomic clocks, referenced to UTC(NBS), at this site to generate the time code. The time code includes a sync word, a time-of-year message (including day of year, hour, minute, and second), UTI correction, and satellite position.

## noch: USA

## USA cont.

Der Satellit hat eine Höhe von ca. 36 000 km über dem Äquator. Das von der Bodenstation auf Wallops Island, Virginia, erzeugte und vom Satelliten empfangene und wiederausgestrahlte Zeitsignal benötigt daher bis zum Eintreffen beim terrestrischen Empfänger mindestens eine Zeit von 260 ms. Um diese Laufzeitdifferenz auszugleichen, sendet Wallops Island absichtlich die Zeitsignale 260 ms zu früh zum GOES-Satelliten. Im gesamten Empfangsgebiet der Satelliten können die Signale durch diese Korrektur mit einer maximalen Verzögerung von 16 ms empfangen werden.

The satellite has reached a position at about 36 000 km above the equator. The signal emitted at the ground station at Wallops Island, Virginia is relayed by the GOES-Satellite and reaches the receiver on the ground at least 260 ms later. To compare this lateness of 260 ms, Wallops Islands intentionally transmits its signal to the GOES satellite 260 ms in front of the real time. In the whole coverage area thus the maximum delay is less than 16 ms.

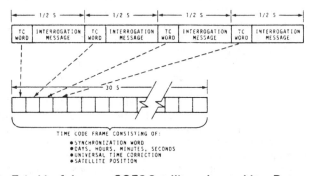

**Zeitablauf der vom GOES-Satelliten abgestrahlten Daten**
**The GOES interrogation channel format**

TIME CODE FORMAT

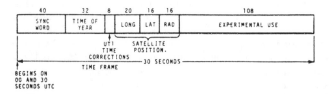

**Die GOES-Zeitdaten ("TC Word")**
**The GOES time code format ("TC Word")**

## Die Versorgungsgebiete der GOES-Satelliten
## The GOES Satellites' Coverage Area

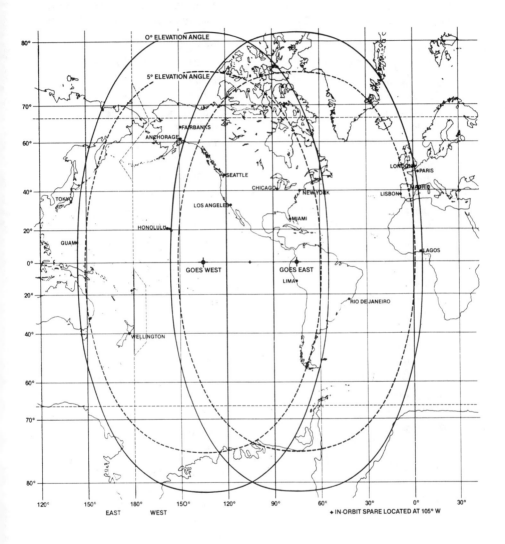

## UdSSR:

The State Committee of Standards of the Council of Ministers of the USSR, 9 Leninsky Prospekt, 117049 Moskau

1.) Station:
RBU        66.66 kHz

Sendeleistung:
10 kW

Senderstandort:
Moskau

G. K.: 55° 48' N, 38° 18' Ost

Sendezeiten:
ständig

Wartungspausen:
Jeder zweite Dienstag jeden geraden Monats 05.00-13.00 UTC

Sendeschema:
siehe Diagramm

2.) Station:
RTZ        50 kHz

Sendeleistung:
10 kW

Senderstandort:
Irkutsk

G. K.: 52° 26' N, 104° 02' Ost

Sendezeiten:
01.00-24.00 UTC

Wartungspausen:
Jeder 1., 3. und 4. Montag im Monat. Im Mai jeder 3., 4. und 5. Montag von 0.00 bis 08.00 UTC

Sendeschema:
siehe Diagramm

3.) Station:
RW166      200 kHz

Sendeleistung:
40 kW

Senderstandort:
Irkutsk

Sendezeiten:
22.00-21.00 UTC

## USSR:

The State Committee of Standards of the Council of Ministers of the USSR, 9 Leninsky Prospekt, 117049 Moscow

1.) Station:
RBU        66.66 kHz

Power:
10 kW

Location:
Moscow

G. C.: 55° 48' N, 38° 18' E

Times:
continuous

Maintenance breaks:
each 2nd Tuesday of each even month 05.00-13.00 UTC

Type of transmission:
to be explained lateron!

2.) Station:
RTZ        50 kHz

Power:
10 kW

Location:
Irkutsk

G. C.: 52° 26' N, 104° 02' E

Times:
01.00-24.00 UTC

Maintenance breaks:
each 1st, 3rd and 4th Monday of the month (in May: 3rd, 4th and 5th Monday) 00.00-08.00 UTC

Type of transmission:
to be explained lateron!

3.) Station:
RW166      200 kHz

Power:
40 kW

Location:
Irkutsk

Times:
22.00-21.00 UTC

**4.) Station:**
RW 76     272 kHz

Sendeleistung:
—?—

Senderstandort:
Nowosibirsk

Sendezeiten:
22.00-20.00 UTC

Sendeschema:
siehe Diagramm

**4.) Station:**
RW 76     272 kHz

Power:
—?—

Location:
Novosibirsk

Times:
22.00-20.00 UTC

Type of transmission:
to be explained later on!

**5.) Station:**
RWM     4996 kHz     5 kW
        9996 kHz     5 kW
        14996 kHz    8 kW

Senderstandort:
Moskau

G. K.: 55° 48' N, 38° 18' Ost

Sendezeiten:
ständig

Wartungspausen:
Auf 4996 kHz an jedem ersten Mittwoch des ersten Monats jeden Vierteljahres 05.00-13.00 UTC
Auf 9996 kHz wie vor, jedoch jeder zweite Mittwoch statt jeder erste Mittwoch.
Auf 14996 kHz an jedem dritten Mittwoch jeden ungeraden Monats 05.00-13.00 UTC.

Sendeschema:
siehe Diagramm

**5.) Station:**
RWM     4996 kHz     5 kW
        9996 kHz     5 kW
        14996 kHz    8 kW

Location:
Moskow

G. C.: 55° 48' N, 38° 18' E

Times:
24 h daily

Maintenance breaks:
RWM 4996 kHz each 1st Wednesday of each 1st month of each quarter of the year 05.00-13.00 UTC;
RWM 9996 kHz each 2nd Wednesday of each 1st month of each quarter of the year 05.00-13.00 UTC;
RWM 14996 kHz each 3rd Wednesday of each odd month 05.00-13.00 UTC.

Type of transmission:
to be explained later on!

**6.) Station:**
RID     5004 kHz
        10004 kHz
        15004 kHz

**6.) Station:**
RID     5004 kHz
        10004 kHz
        15004 kHz

# noch: UdSSR

Sendeleistung:
1 kW

Senderstandort:
Irkutsk

G. K.: 52° 26′ N, 104° 02′ Ost

Sendezeiten:
ständig

Wartungspausen:
Auf 5004 kHz an jedem 1. und
4. Dienstag des Monats
00.00-08.00 UTC.
Auf 10004 kHz an jedem 2. und
4. Dienstag des Monats
00.00-08.00 UTC.
Auf 15004 kHz an jedem 3. und
4. Dienstag des Monats
00.00-08.00 UTC.

Sendeschema:
siehe Diagramm

7.) Station:
RTA     10000 kHz
        15000 kHz

Sendeleistung:
5 kW

Senderstandort:
Novosibirsk

G. K.: 55° 04′ N, 82° 58′ Ost

Sendezeiten:
Auf 10000 kHz    02.00-05.00 UTC
                 14.00-17.30 UTC
                 18.00-01.30 UTC
Auf 15000 kHz    06.30-09.30 UTC
                 10.00-13.30 UTC
Während der Sommerzeit auf beiden
Frequenzen jeweils eine Stunde später.

Wartungspausen:
An jedem 1. und 3. Donnerstag des
Monats 00.00-10.00 UTC

Sendeschema:
siehe Diagramm

# USSR cont.

Power:
1 kW

Location:
Irkutsk

G. C.: 52° 26′ N, 104° 02′ E

Times:
24 h daily

Maintenance breaks:
RID 5004 kHz each 1st and 4th
Tuesday of each month
00.00-08.00 UTC;
RID 10004 kHz each 2nd and 4th
Tuesday of each month
00.00-08.00 UTC;
RID 15004 kHz each 3rd and 4th
Tuesday of each month
00.00-08.00 UTC.

Type of transmission:
to be explained later on!

7.) Station:
RTA     10000 kHz
        15000 kHz

Power:
5 kW

Location:
Novosibirsk

G. C.: 55° 04′ N, 82° 58′ E

Times:
On 10000 kHz    02.00-05.00 UTC
                14.00-17.30 UTC
                18.00-01.30 UTC
On 15000 kHz    06.30-09.30 UTC
                10.00-13.30 UTC

During daylight saving time one
hour later.

Maintenance breaks:
each 1st and 3rd Thursday of each
month at 00.00-10.00 UTC

Type of transmission:
to be explained later on!

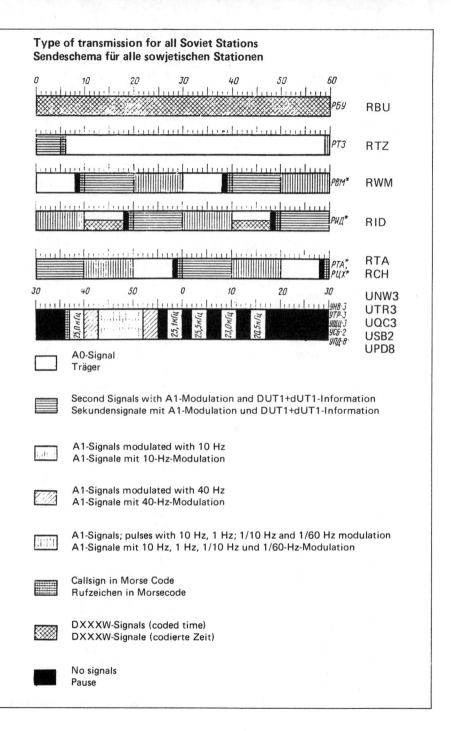

## Type of transmission for all Soviet Stations
## Sendeschema für alle sowjetischen Stationen

| | | |
|---|---|---|
| РБУ | RBU |
| РТ3 | RTZ |
| РВМ* | RWM |
| РИД* | RID |
| РТА*,<br>РЦХ* | RTA<br>RCH |
| УНВ-3<br>УТР-3<br>УЩЩ-3<br>УСБ-2<br>УПД-8 | UNW3<br>UTR3<br>UQC3<br>USB2<br>UPD8 |

A0-Signal
Träger

Second Signals with A1-Modulation and DUT1+dUT1-Information
Sekundensignale mit A1-Modulation und DUT1+dUT1-Information

A1-Signals modulated with 10 Hz
A1-Signale mit 10-Hz-Modulation

A1-Signals modulated with 40 Hz
A1-Signale mit 40-Hz-Modulation

A1-Signals; pulses with 10 Hz, 1 Hz; 1/10 Hz and 1/60 Hz modulation
A1-Signale mit 10 Hz, 1 Hz, 1/10 Hz und 1/60-Hz-Modulation

Callsign in Morse Code
Rufzeichen in Morsecode

DXXXW-Signals (coded time)
DXXXW-Signale (codierte Zeit)

No signals
Pause

8.) Station:
   RCH      2500 kHz
              5000 kHz
              10000 kHz

Sendeleistung:
1 kW

Senderstandort:
Taschkent

G. K.: 41$^o$ 19′ N, 69$^o$ 15′ Ost

Sendezeiten:
Auf   2500 kHz    05.30-04.00 UTC
Auf   5000 kHz    02.00-04.00 UTC
                     14.00-17.30 UTC
                     18.00-01.30 UTC
Auf 10000 kHz    05.30-09.30 UTC
                     10.00-13.30 UTC
Während der Sommerzeit auf allen Frequenzen jeweils eine Stunde später.

Wartungspausen:
An jedem 3. Montag des Monats 01.00-11.00 UTC

Sendeschema:
siehe Diagramm

8.) Station:
   RCH      2500 kHz
              5000 kHz
              10000 kHz

Power:
1 kW

Location:
Tashkent

G. C.: 41$^o$ 19′ N, 69$^o$ 15′ E

Times:
On   2500 kHz    05.30-04.00 UTC
On   5000 kHz    02.00-04.00 UTC
                     14.00-17.30 UTC
                     18.00-01.30 UTC
On 10000 kHz    05.30-09.30 UTC
                     10.00-13.30 UTC
During daylight saving time one hour later.

Maintenance breaks:
each 3rd Monday of each month at 01.00-11.00 UTC

Type of transmission:
to be explained later on!

9.) Station:
   UTR3     25.0 kHz, 25.1 kHz,
               25.5 kHz, 23.0 kHz,
               20.5 kHz

Sendeleistung:
300 kW

Senderstandort:
Gorki

G. K.: 56$^o$ 11′ N, 43$^o$ 58′ Ost

Sendezeiten:
05.36-06.17 UTC
13.36-14.17 UTC
18.36-19.17 UTC
    während der Normalzeit
07.36-08.17 UTC
14.36-15.17 UTC
19.36-20.17 UTC
    während der Sommerzeit

9.) Station:
   UTR3     25.0 kHz, 25.1 kHz,
               25.5 kHz, 23.0 kHz,
               20.5 kHz

Power:
300 kW

Location:
Gorki

G. C.: 56$^o$ 11′ N, 43$^o$ 58′ E

Times:
05.36-06.17 UTC
13.36-14.17 UTC
18.36-19.17 UTC
    normal time
07.36-08.17 UTC
14.36-15.17 UTC
19.36-20.17 UTC
    during daylight saving time

Wartungspausen:
Jeder 8., 18. und 28. des Monats
ganztägig 00.00-24.00 Uhr Moskauer
Zeit

Sendeschema:
siehe Diagramm

Maintenance breaks:
each 8th, 18th and 28th of each
month 24 h that day (Moscow-Time!)

Type of transmission:
to be explained later on!

---

10.) Station:

UQC3    25.0 kHz, 25.1 kHz,
25.5 kHz, 23.0 kHz,
20.5 kHz

Sendeleistung:
300 kW

Senderstandort:
Khabarovsk

G. K.: 48° 30′ N, 134° 51′ Ost

Sendezeiten:
00.36-01.17 UTC
06.36-07.17 UTC
17.36-18.17 UTC
   während der Normalzeit
02.36-03.17 UTC
06.36-07.17 UTC
18.36-19.17 UTC
   während der Sommerzeit

Wartungspausen:
Jeder 10., 20. und 30. des Monats
ganztägig 00.00-24.00 Uhr Moskauer Zeit

Sendeschema:
siehe Diagramm

10.) Station:

UQC3    25.0 kHz, 25.1 kHz,
25.5 kHz, 23.0 kHz,
20.5 kHz

Power:
300 kW

Location:
Chabarovsk

G. C.: 48° 30′ N, 134° 51′ E

Times:
00.36-01.17 UTC
06.36-07.17 UTC
17.36-18.17 UTC
   normal time
02.36-03.17 UTC
06.36-07.17 UTC
18.36-19.17 UTC
   during daylight saving time

Maintenance breaks:
each 10th, 20th and 30th of each
month 24 h that day (Moscow-
Time!)

Type of transmission:
to be explained later on!

---

11.) Station:

UPD 8    25.0, 25.1., 25.5., 23.0,
20.5 kHz

Sendeleistung:
300 kW

Senderstandort:
Archangelsk

G. K.: 64° 24′ N, 41° 32′ Ost

11.) Station:

UPD8    25.0, 25.1, 25.5, 23.0,
20.5 kHz

Power:
300 kW

Location:
Archangelsk

G. C.: 64° 24′ N, 41° 32′ E

Sendezeiten:
08.36-09.17 UTC
11.36-12.17 UTC
    während der Normalzeit
09.36-10.17 UTC
12.36-13.17 UTC
    während der Sommerzeit
Wartungspausen:
Jeder 4., 14. und 24. des Monats
ganztägig Moskauer Zeit

Times:
08.36-09.17 UTC
11.36-12.17 UTC
    normal time
09.36-10.17 UTC
12.36-13.17 UTC
    during daylight saving time
Maintenance breaks:
each 4th, 14th and 24th
of the month (Moscow Time)

12.) Station:
USB2     25.0, 25.1, 25.5, 23.0,
         20.5 kHz

Sendeleistung:
300 kW

Senderstandort:
Frunze

G.K.: 43° 04' N, 73° 39' Ost

Sendezeiten:
04.36-05.17 UTC
09.36-10.17 UTC
20.36-21.17 UTC
    während der Normalzeit
05.36-06.17 UTC
11.36-12.17 UTC
23.36-24.17 UTC
    während der Sommerzeit

Wartungspausen:
Jeder 6., 16. und 26. des Monats
ganztägig Moskauer Zeit

12.) Station:
USB2     25.0, 25.1, 25.5, 23.0
         20.5 kHz

Power:
300 kW

Location:
Frunze

G. C.: 43° 04' N, 73° 39' E

Times:
04.36-05.17 UTC
09.36-10.17 UTC
20.36-21.17 UTC
    normal time
05.36-06.17 UTC
11.36-12.17 UTC
23.36-24.17 UTC
    during daylight saving time

Maintenance breaks:
Each 6th, 16th and 26th of the
month (Moscow Time)

## Venezuela:

Dirección de Hidrografia y Navegación, Observatorio Cagigal, Apartado Postal No. 6745, Caracas

Station:
YVTO   6100 kHz

G. K.: 10° 30′ N, 66° 56′ W

Sendeleistung:
1 kW

Sendezeiten:
ständig

Sendeschema:
Sekundenimpulse von 100 ms Länge mit 1000 Hz Modulation. Minutenimpulse von 500 ms Länge mit 800 Hz Modulation. Der Sekundenimpuls 30 fehlt. Zwischen der 52. und 57. Sekunde jeder Minute erfolgt in spanischer Sprache die Zeitangabe in Stunden, Minuten und Sekunden.

Bestätigung:
per QSL-Karte

## Venezuela:

Dirección de Hidrografia y Navegación, Observatorio Cagigal, Apartado Postal No. 6745, Caracas

Station:
YVTO   6100 kHz

G. C.: 10° 30′ N, 66° 56′ W

Power:
1 kW

Times:
continuous

Type of transmission:
Second pulses of 1000 Hz modulation with 100 ms duration. Minutes are identified by 800 Hz tones of 500 ms duration. Second 30 is omitted. Voice announcement of the hour, minute and second is given each minute between seconds 52 and 57 in Spanish.

V.
by QSL, Rp

# 7. Frequenzliste      7. Frequency list

| | | | | | | |
|---|---|---|---|---|---|---|
| 16 | GBR | Greenwich | | HLA | Taedok Science Town |
| 20.5 | UNW3 | several | | IAM | Rome |
| 23.0 | UPD8 | stations | | IBF | Turine |
| 25.0 | USB2 | in | | JJY | Tokyo |
| 25.1 | USZ3 | the | | LOL1 | Buenos Aires |
| 25.5 | UTR3 | USSR | | MSF | Teddington |
| 40 | JG2AS | Sanwa | | RCH | Tashkent |
| 50 | OMA | Liblice | | WWV | Fort Collins |
| | RTZ | Irkutsk | | WWVH | Hawaii |
| 60 | MSF | Teddington | | ZUO | Pretoria |
| | WWVB | Fort Collins | 5004 | RID | Irkutsk |
| 66.66 | RBU | Moscow | 5430 | BPM | Lintong |
| 75 | HBG | Neuchâtel | 6100 | YVTO | Caracas |
| 77.5 | DCF77 | Mainflingen | 6428.5 | NPG | Stockton |
| 200 | RW166 | Irkutsk | 6454 | XSG | Shanghai |
| 272 | RW76 | Novosibirsk | 6649 | | Belconnen |
| 338 | | Hong Kong | 6679 | | Hong Kong |
| 418 | ZSC | Capetown | 6840 | EBC | San Fernando |
| 434 | VWC | Calcutta | 7335 | CHU | Ottawa |
| 435 | PPR | Rio de Janeiro | 7600 | HD2IOA | Guayaquil |
| 482 | 4PB | Colombo | 8000 | JJY | Tokyo |
| 485 | OBC | Callao | 8030 | LOL3 | Buenos Aires |
| 500 | VPS | Hong Kong | 8461 | ZSC | Capetown |
| 522.5 | XSG | Shanghai | 8473 | 4PB | Colombo |
| 2500 | BPM | Lintong | 8487 | XSG | Shanghai |
| | MSF | Teddington | 8539 | VPS35 | Hong Kong |
| | OMA | Liblice | 8542 | PKI | Jakarta |
| | RCH | Tashkent | 8650 | OBC | Callao |
| | WWV | Fort Collins | 8677 | CBV | Playa Ancha |
| | WWVH | Hawaii | 8721 | PPE | Rio de Janeiro |
| | ZUO | Pretoria | 8823 | | Hong Kong |
| 3170 | OLB5 | Liblice | 9277.5 | NPG | Stockton |
| 3268 | NPG | Stockton | 9351 | BPM | Lintong |
| 3330 | CHU | Ottawa | 9996 | RWM | Moscow |
| 3810 | HD2IOA | Guayaquil | 10000 | ATA | New Delhi |
| 4228 | CBV | Playa Ancha | | BPM | Lintong |
| 4232.5 | VPS8 | Hong Kong | | JJY | Tokyo |
| 4244 | PPR | Rio de Janeiro | | LOL1 | Buenos Aires |
| 4286 | VWC | Calcutta | | MSF | Teddington |
| 4291 | ZSC | Capetown | | RTA | Novosibirsk |
| 4445 | NPO | San Miguel | | RCH | Tashkent |
| 4525 | Y3S | Nauen | | WWV | Fort Collins |
| 4856 | LOL2 | Buenos Aires | | WWVH | Hawaii |
| 4996 | RWM | Moscow | 10004 | RID | Irkutsk |
| 5000 | ATA | New Delhi | 10440.5 | NPO | San Miguel |
| | BPM | Lintong | (11173.5 | EBC | San Fernando) |
| | BSF | Taipei | 11440 | PLC | Jakarta |
| | HD2IOA | Guayaquil | 12008 | EBC | San Fernando |

| | | | | | | |
|---|---|---|---|---|---|---|
| 12307 | OBC | Callao | | 16938 | XSG | Shanghai |
| 12724 | ZSC | Capetown | | 17018 | ZSC | Capetown |
| 12745 | VWC | Calcutta | | 17096 | VPS80 | Hong Kong |
| 12804 | NPO | San Miguel | | 17180 | LOL3 | Buenos Aires |
| 12954 | XSG | Shanghai | | 17194.4 | PPR | Rio de Janeiro |
| 12966 | NPG | Stockton | | 20000 | WWV | Fort Collins |
| 12982 | | Belconnen | | 22455 | ZSC | Capetown |
| 13020.5 | VPS60 | Hong Kong | | 22536 | VPS225 | Hong Kong |
| 13105 | PPR | Rio de Janeiro | | 22603 | PPR | Rio de Janeiro |
| 13282 | | Hong Kong | | | | |
| 14670 | CHU | Ottawa | | | | |
| 14996 | RWM | Moscow | | MHz | | |
| 15000 | ATA | New Delhi | | 95.000 | | Hong Kong |
| | BPM | Lintong | | 100.000 | ZUO | Pretoria |
| | BSF | Taipei | | 160.230 | | Rio de Janeiro |
| | JJY | Tokyo | | 166.530 | | Rio de Janeiro |
| | LOL1 | Buenos Aires | | 171.130 | | Rio de Janeiro |
| | RTA | Novosibirsk | | 468.8250 | GOES (western) Satellite | |
| | WWV | Fort Collins | | 468.8375 | GOES (eastern) Satellite | |
| | WWVH | Hawaii | | 1227.600 | NAVSTAR GPS-Satellites | |
| 15004 | RID | Irkutsk | | 1575.420 | NAVSTAR GPS-Satellites | |

## 8. Rundfunksender mit präzisen Zeitsignalen

## 8. Broadcasting Radio Stations transmitting high-precision time signals

### Argentinien

Stationen:
  Radio Nacional LRA      870 kHz
                 LRA31 6060 kHz
Zeiten:
  LRA    H+00, H-30  1100-0400 Uhr UTC
  LRA31 H+00, H+30 1100-0300 Uhr UTC
Sendeschema:
  siehe Diagramm

### Argentine

Stations:
  Radio Nacional LRA      870 kHz
                 LRA31 6060 kHz
Times:
  LRA    H+00, H+30  1100-0400 UTC
  LRA31 H+00, H+30  1100-0300 UTC
Type of transmission:
  as shown in the diagram

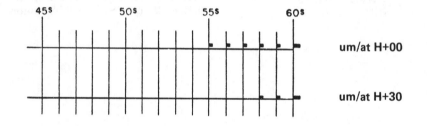

um/at H+00

um/at H+30

# Deutschland (BRD)

Station:
Deutschlandfunk, Köln
Frequenzen:
153, 209, 549, 756, 1269, 1539 kHz
u. UKW
Zeiten:
0000, 0600, 1200, 1800 Uhr Lokalzeit
Sendeschema:
siehe Diagramm

# Germany (Fed. Rep.)

Station:
Deutschlandfunk, Cologne
Frequencies:
153, 209, 549, 756, 1269, 1539 kHz
+ FM
Times:
0000, 0600, 1200, 1800 hours local time
Type of transmission:
as shown in the diagram

Station:
Westdeutscher Rundfunk, Köln
Norddeutscher Rundfunk, Hamburg
Frequenzen:
702, 828, 972, 1593 kHz u. UKW
Zeiten:
0500, 0600, 0700, 1300, 1900,
2400 Uhr Lokalzeit
Sendeschema:
siehe Diagramm des DLF

Station:
Westdeutscher Rundfunk, Cologne
Norddeutscher Rundfunk, Hamburg
Frequencies:
702, 828, 972, 1593 kHz + various FM
Times:
0500, 0600, 0700, 1300, 1900,
2400 hours local time
Type of transmission:
see under Deutschlandfunk above

# Deutschland (DDR)

Station:
  Stimme der DDR
Frequenzen:
  173, 783, 1359 kHz und verschiedene
  UKW-Frequenzen
Zeiten:
  täglich in den 30 Sekunden vor 0600,
  1200 und 1800 Uhr UTC. Während der
  Sommerzeit eine Stunde früher.
Sendeschema:
  Siehe Diagramm. Die Sekunden-
  impulse haben eine Länge von 100 ms,
  der Minutenimpuls hat eine Länge von
  500 ms.

# Germany (Dem. Rep.)

Station:
  Stimme der DDR
Frequencies:
  173, 783, 1359 kHz + various FM
  frequencies
Times:
  daily at the 30 seconds before 0600,
  1200 and 1800 UTC. During daylight
  saving time one hour earlier.
Type of transmission:
  As shown in the diagram. The seconds
  pulses have a duration of 100 ms,
  the minute pulse has a duration of
  500 ms.

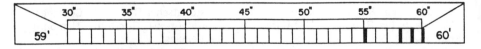

**Sendeschema aller DDR-Stationen**    **Transmission schedule of all GDR-Stations**

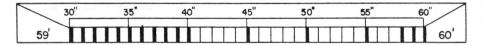

Zusätzlich um 0300, 0400, 0500, 0700,
0900, 1400, 1600 Uhr sendet die Stimme
der DDR diese Impulse

In addition at 0300, 0400, 0500, 0700,
0900, 1400, 1600 h the Voice of GDR
is transmitting these time pulses

Station:
  Berliner Rundfunk
Frequenzen:
  657, 693, 999, 1170, 1431, 1575 kHz
  und verschiedene UKW-Frequenzen
Zeiten:
  täglich in den fünf Sekunden vor 0300,
  0400, 0500, 0600, 1100 und 1200 Uhr
  UTC. Während der Sommerzeit eine
  Stunde früher.
Sendeschema:
  Siehe Diagramm

Station:
  Berliner Rundfunk
Frequencies:
  657, 693, 999, 1170, 1431, 1575 kHz
  + various FM frequencies
Times:
  daily at the 5 seconds before 0300,
  0400, 0500, 0600, 1100 and 1200
  UTC. During daylight saving time
  one hour earlier.
Type of transmission:
  as shown in the diagram.

Station:
Radio DDR1
Frequenzen:
531, 558, 576, 603, 792, 882,
1044 kHz und verschiedene UKW-
Frequenzen
Zeiten:
Zu jeder vollen Stunde zwischen 0300
und 2200 Uhr UTC. Während der Sommerzeit eine Stunde früher.
Sendeschema:
Siehe Berliner Rundfunk

Station:
Radio DDR1
Frequencies:
531, 558, 576, 603, 792, 882,
1044 kHz + various FM frequencies
Times:
Every hour between 0300 and 2200
hours UTC. During daylight saving
time one hour earlier.
Type of transmission:
See Berliner Rundfunk


## Frankreich

Centre National d'Etudes des Télé-
communications, PAB-STC-Etalons
de Fréquence et de Temps,
196, rue de Paris, F-92220 Bagneux

Station:
TDF Allouis
G.K.: 47° 10′ N, 2° 12′ Ost
Frequenz: 162 kHz
Zeiten:
ständig, außer dienstags
von 0100 bis 0500 Uhr
Sendeschema:
Der Träger ist phasenmoduliert mit
Sekundenimpulsen von 100 ms Dauer.
Der 59ste Impuls jeder Minute fehlt.
Die Zeit wird codiert übertragen,
indem die Modulation für Binär 1 mit
doppelter Modulation gesendet wird.
Die Angaben für die Minute, Stunde,
den Tag, Wochentag, Monat und das
Jahr werden codiert zwischen dem
21sten und 58sten Sekundenimpuls
übertragen. Wenn der 17te Impuls den
Binärwert 1 enthält, so wird damit
mitgeteilt, daß in Frankreich die
Sommerzeit gerade herrscht. Binär 1
des 18ten Impulses steht für Normal-
(Winter)zeit. Ist der 14te Impuls mit
Binär 1 übertragen, so handelt es sich
um einen Feiertag in Frankreich
(z. B. Weihnachten, 14. Juli usw.).

## France

Centre National d'Etudes des Télé-
communications, PAB-STC-Etalons
de Fréquence et de Temps,
196, rue de Paris, F-92220 Bagneux

Station:
TDF Allouis
G.C.: 47° 10′ N, 2° 12′ E
Frequency: 162 kHz
Times:
continuous, except every tuesday
from 1 h to 5 h
Type of transmission:
Phase modulation of the carrier by
+ an − 1 radion in 0.1s every second
except the 59th second of each
minute. This modulation is doubled to
indicate binary 1. The numbers of the
minute, hour, day of the month, day
of the week, month and year are
transmitted each minute from the
21st to the 58th second, in accordance
with the French legal time scale. In
addition, a binary 1 at the 17th second
indicates that the local time is 2 hours
ahead of UTC (summertime), a binary 1
at the 18 th second indicates when
the local time is one hour ahead
of UTC (wintertime); a binary 1 at the
14th second indicates that the current
day is a public holiday (christmas,
14th July e.t.c.).

# Großbritannien

Station:
  BBC London
Zeiten:

  BBC Radio 1: Mo-Fr 0600, 0700, 0800, 1000, 1100, 1400, 2200, 2400 h
  Sat 0700, 1300, 1930, 2200, 2400
  Sun 0700, 1000, 1700, 1900, 2200, 2400 h

  BBC Radio 2: Mo-Fri 0500, 0600, 0700, 1400, 1800, 1900, 2200, 2400 h
  Sat 0700, 0800, 1000, 1200, 1300, 1800, 1930, 2400 h
  Sun 0700, 1000, 1200, 1400, 1700, 1900, 2200, 2400 h

  BBC Radio 3: Mo-Fr 0700, 0800, 0900 h
  Sat + Sun 0800, 0900 h

  BBC Radio 4: Mo-Fri 0600, 0700, 0800, 0900, 1000, 1100, 1200, 1300,
  1400, 1500, 1700, 1800, 1900, 2200 h
  Sat 0700, 0800, 0900, 1200, 1300, 1400, 1600, 1800 h
  Sun 0800, 0900, 1300, 1400, 1600, 1800, 2100 h

  BBC External Services:
  Mo-Fri On the hour (except 0200, 1100, 1500, 2200 h)
  Sat On the hour (except 0200, 1100, 1300, 1500, 2000, 2200 h)
  Sun On the hour (except 0200, 100, 1500, 1800, 2000, 2200 h)

Sendeschema:
  5 kurze Impulse in den Sekunden 55 bis 59, gefolgt von einem längeren Impuls, der die Minute markiert. Die kurzen Impulse haben eine Länge von 100 ms, der längere Impuls hat eine Länge von 500 ms.

# Great Britain

Station:
  BBC London
Times:

Type of transmission:
  Time signals consisting of 5 short pips, from second 55 to second 59, followed by a lengthened pip, the start of which is marking the minute. The short pips have a duration of 100 ms, the long pip has a duration of 500 ms.

# Hong Kong

Station:
  Radio Television Hong Kong
Frequenzen:
  567 kHz, 91,00 MHz
Zeiten:
  0000-2300 Uhr zu jeder vollen Stunde

Frequenzen:
  783 kHz, 94,00 MHz, 96,00 MHz
Zeiten:
  wie vorstehend; zusätzlich um 1530, 1630, 1730 Uhr

# Hong Kong

Station:
  Radio Television Hong Kong
Frequency:
  567 kHz, 91.00 MHz
Times:
  0000-2300 hours on the hour

Frequency:
  783 kHz, 94.00 MHz, 96.00 MHz
Times:
  as above; additionally at 1530, 1630, 1730 h

# Italien

Station:
  Radiotelevisione Italiana, Rom (RAI)

Zeiten:
  „Radio 1":     0500, 0600, 0700, 0900, 1100, 1200, 1300, 1400, 1600, 1800, 2200 h
  „Radio 2":     0530, 0630, 0730, 0830, 0900, 1030, 1130, 1230, 1430, 1530, 1630, 1730, 1830, 2130 h
  „Radio 3":     0545, 0625, 0845, 1045, 1415, 1745, 1945, 2245 h
  „Notturno Italiano":     2300, 2400, 0100, 0200, 0300, 0400 h

Sendeschema:
  siehe Diagramm. Die Impulse haben
  eine Länge von 100 ms und 1000 Hz
  Modulation.

# Italy

Station:
  Radiotelevisione Italiana, Rome (RAI)

Times:
  „Radio 1":     0500, 0600, 0700, 0900, 1100, 1200, 1300, 1400, 1600, 1800, 2200 h
  „Radio 2":     0530, 0630, 0730, 0830, 0900, 1030, 1130, 1230, 1430, 1530, 1630, 1730, 1830, 2130 h
  „Radio 3":     0545, 0625, 0845, 1045, 1415, 1745, 1945, 2245 h
  „Notturno Italiano":     2300, 2400, 0100, 0200, 0300, 0400 h

Type of transmission:
  As shown in the diagram. The time
  pips have a duration of 100 ms and
  a modulation of 1000 Hz.

```
50 s        55 s        60 s
```

# Neuseeland

Department of Scientific and Industrial
Research, Geophysics Division,
P.O.Box 1320, Wellington

Die in der 10. Ausgabe von Zeitzeichensendern vermerkte Station hat die Zeitzeichenaussendungen auf 417.5 kHz.
eingestellt, produziert aber weiterhin
Zeitsignale, die bei Bedarf vom National
Broadcasting Network und einigen
privaten Stationen ausgestrahlt werden.
Um 2300 UTC werden drei Gruppen
von Zeitsignalen gegen Ende der 57sten,
58sten und 60sten Minute ausgestrahlt.
Die mit 1 kHz modulierten Sekundensignale sind 150 ms lang, die Minuten-
signale sind 300 ms lang.

# New Zealand

Department of Scientific and Industrial
Research, Geophysics Division,
P.O.Box 1320, Wellington

The station mentioned in the 10th
edition of Time Signal Stations no
longer transmits time signals on
417.5 kHz. The time service generates
time signals on the hour which are
distributed throughout New Zealand
and transmitted by broadcasting stations
of the National Broadcasting Network,
plus a few private stations.
At 2300 UTC 3 sets of time pips are
sent at the end of the 57th, 58th and
59th minute. The time pips are 1 kHz
sine wave and are 150 ms long, except
the sixth pip which is 300 ms long.

## Polen

Polskie Radio I Telewizja, Warschau
Stationen:
227, 738, 819, 1080, 1206, 1305,
1368 kHz
Zeiten:
Auf 227 kHz:
werktags 0400, 0500, 0600, 0700, 0800,
0900, 1000, 1200, 1300, 1400, 1500,
1600, 1700, 1800, 1900, 2200 Uhr
(samstags nicht zu den unterstrichenen
Zeiten)
sonntags 0500, 1000, 1400, 1600, 1900,
2000, 2100, 2300 Uhr
Auf Mittelwelle:
wochentags 0600, 1200, 1400, 1500,
1600, 1800, 2000, 2300 Uhr
(samstags nicht um 2300 Uhr)
sonntags 0500, 1000, 1400, 1600, 1900,
2000, 2100, 2300 Uhr
Sendeschema:
Zeitimpulse zu den Sekunden 55 bis 60

## Poland

Polskie Radio I Telewizja, Warsaw
Stations:
227, 738, 819, 1080, 1206, 1260, 1305,
1368 kHz
Times:
On 227 kHz:
weekdays 0400, 0500, 0600, 0700, 080
0800, 0900, 1000, 1200, 1300, 1400,
1500, 1600, 1700, 1800, 1900, 2200 h
(the underlined times not on saturdays)
sundays 0500, 1000, 1400, 1600,
1900, 2000, 2100, 2300 h
On Mediumwave:
weekdays 0600, 1200, 1400, 1500,
1600, 1800, 2000, 2300 h (2300 h
(2300 h not on saturdays)
sundays 0500, 1000, 1400, 1600,
1900, 2000, 2100, 2300 h
Type of transmission:
Time pips at the seconds 55, 56, 57,
58, 59 and 60

## Schweden

Sveriges Radio, Stockholm
Stationen:
191 kHz (SBG) Motala
981 kHz (SBB) Göteborg
1179 kHz (SBH) Hörby
Zeiten:
11h 58m 55s – 11h 58m 16s täglich
Sendeschema:
Siehe Diagramm. DUT1 wird im CCIR-
code übertragen, indem die entsprechenden Sekunden in der Modulation
geändert werden. Normalmodulation
1000 Hz, DUT1-Modulation 600 Hz

## Sweden

Sveriges Radio, Stockholm
Stations:
191 kHz (SBG) Motala
981 kHz (SBB) Göteborg
1179 kHz (SBH) Hörby
Times:
11h 58m 55s – 11 h 59m 16s daily
Type of transmission:
As shown in the diagram. DUT1 is
indicated by emphasizing a number
of consecutive seconds markers by
tone modulation. CCIR-code. The
normal pulses are modulated by
1000 Hz, the emphasized pulses by
600 Hz.

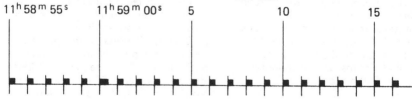

11^h 58^m 55^s          11^h 59^m 00^s     5          10          15

# Tschechoslowakei

Tschechoslowakischer Rundfunk, Prag
Stationen:
272, 639, 702, 954, 1098, 1233,
1287, 1521 kHz
Sendeschema:
6 Impulse von je 100 ms Dauer in den
Sekunden 55, 56, 57, 58, 59 und 60
zum Ende jeder vollen Viertelstunde.
Modulationsfrequenz 1000 Hz.
Die Zeitsignale werden in das Programm
eingestreut, wenn es das Programm
ermöglicht.

# Czechoslovakia

Czechoslovak Radio, Prague
Stations:
272, 639, 702, 954, 1098, 1233,
1287, 1521 kHz
Type of transmission:
6 pips of 100 ms duration at the
seconds 55, 56, 57, 58, 59 and 60
at the end of each quarter hour.
Modulation frequency 1000 Hz.
The time signals are included into
the radio programme whenever possible.

# Uruguay

S.O.D.R.E., Montevideo
Stationen:
CX 6                     650 kHz
CXA 6                    9620 kHz
Zeiten:
1500 und 2000 Uhr UTC täglich
Sendeschema:
Von 59 m 40 s bis 59 m 50 s ein langer
Ton, in der 55sten bis 59sten Sekunde
je ein Sekundenimpuls, in der 60sten
Sekunde ein langer Impuls.

# Uruguay

S.O.D.R.E., Montevideo
Stations:
CX 6                     650 kHz
CXA 6                    9620 kHz
Times:
1500 and 2000 UTC daily
Type of transmission:
From 59 m 40 s to 59 m 50 s, one
long dash, at 55th, 56th, 57th, 58th
and 59th seconds, one dot, at the
60th second, the pip indicates the hour.

## 9. Elektronische, von Zeitzeichen-<br>sendern gesteuerte Uhren

Während noch vor wenigen Jahren reine Sekunden- und Minutenimpulse ausgestrahlt wurden, gehen nunmehr vermehrt die Zeitzeichensender dazu über, zusätzlich die Zeitinformation in codierter Form zu übertragen. Praktiziert wird dieses Verfahren derzeit von den folgenden Sendern, wobei bevorzugt Längstwellensender dazu eingesetzt werden:

| | | |
|---|---|---|
| CHU | Ottawa | 3300, 7335, 14670 kHz |
| DCF77 | Mainflingen | 77,5 kHz |
| HLA | Korea | 5000 kHz |
| MSF | Teddington | 60 kHz |
| OMA | Liblice | 50 kHz |
| RBU | Moskau | 66,67 kHz |
| TDF | Allouis | 162 kHz |
| WWVB | Fort Collins | 60 kHz |

Nachfolgend stellen wir in alphabetischer Firmenreihenfolge die uns bekannten Uhren vor, die diese codierten Zeitinformationen auswerten können. Die genannten Verkaufspreise bitten wir als grobe Richtpreise anzusehen. Mit der Vorstellung einer Uhr ist keine irgendwie geartete Werbung oder Empfehlung von dieser Seite verbunden.

## 9. Electronic clocks remote<br>controlled by Time Signal Radio<br>Stations

A few years ago, time signal stations only radiated time pulses for the seconds and minute markers. Then additionally some stations started emitting extra time information in a coded format enabling the wireless control of clocks.
At the time being, the following time signal radio stations — especially on VLF — are transmitting coded time information:

| | | |
|---|---|---|
| CHU | Ottawa | 3300, 7335, 14670 kHz |
| DCF77 | Mainflingen | 77.5 kHz |
| HLA | Korea | 5000 kHz |
| MSF | Teddington | 60 kHz |
| OMA | Liblice | 50 kHz |
| RBU | Moscow | 66.67 kHz |
| TDF | Allouis | 162 kHz |
| WWVB | Fort Collins | 60 kHz |

Clocks which can be used for these purposes are presented next in alphabetical order of the manufacturers' names. All sales prices may differ in practise, as the mentioned prices are approximate prices. Neither any valuation nor any recommandation in any kind is to be combined with our presentation.

## BHL Electronique, Zone Industrielle, B.P. 8, F-14 540 Bourguebus, France

Bezeichnung der Uhr:
**Horloge 59 HF**
Empfangbarer Sender:
France Inter 162 kHz
Anzeigen für:
Stunden, Minuten, Sekunden, Tag,
Monat, Jahr, Wochentag
Preis: ca. 9000 FF

Besonderheit:
Die Uhr ist in einem 19-Zoll-Einschub
eingebaut. Zusätzlich erhältlich sind zahlreiche Bauteile, die den Anwendungs-
bereich der Uhr nahezu beliebig erweitern
lassen.

Clock's name:
**Horloge 59 HF**
Receives time signals from:
France Inter 162 kHz
Displays for:
Hour, Minutes, Seconds, Day,
Year, Day of the week
Sales price: approx. 9000 FF

Remarks:
The clock is installed in a 19 inch
rack. There are available a lot of
further elements, which allow
various additional clock functions.

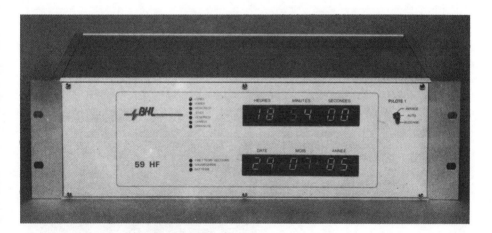

**Braun AG, Postfach 1120,
D-6242 Kronberg im Taunus, BRD**

**Braun AG, P.O.Box 1120,
D-6242 Kronberg im Taunus, FRG**

Bezeichnung der Uhr:
**Funkchronometer**
Empfangbarer Sender:
DCF 77
Anzeigen für:
Stunden, Minuten, Sekunden, Tag,
Monat, Jahr
Preis: entfällt

Clock's name:
**Funkchronometer**
Receives time signals from:
DCF 77
Displays for:
Hours, minutes, seconds, day,
month, year
Sales price: —

Besonderheit:
Bei Senderausfall läuft die Uhr mittels
eingebauten Quarzwerkes selbständig
weiter.
Bei dieser Uhr handelt es sich nur um
einen Prototyp, der bislang nicht in die
Produktion gegangen ist. Die Braun AG
verfolgt das Thema weiter und wird ggf.
später mit einer Funkuhr auf den Markt
kommen.

Remarks:
In the case of a transmitter failure,
the clock continues working
on a built-in quartz-crystal basis.
This clock is a prototype, which did
not got into a mass production yet.
The Braun AG nevertheless is inter-
ested in presenting this or another
type of wireless tuned clocks some-
time in the near future.

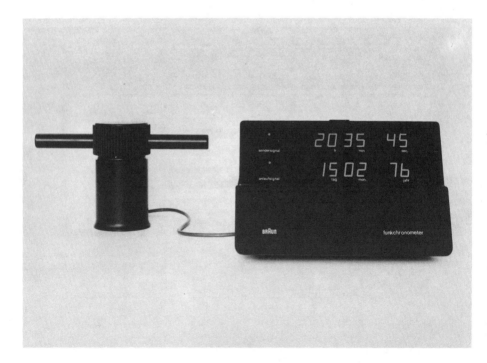

## Cambridge Kits, 45 Old School Lane, Milton, Cambridge, CB4 4BS, England

Bezeichnung der Uhr:
**MSF Clock kit**
Empfangbarer Sender:
MSF 60 kHz
Anzeigen für:
Datum, Stunden, Minuten, Sekunden

Preis:
ca. 85 — 90 Britische Pfund

Besonderheit:
Nur als Bausatz erhältlich

Clock's name:
**MSF Clock kit**
Receives time signals from:
MSF 60 kHz
Displays for:
Date, Hours, Minutes, Seconds

Sales price:
approx. 85 — 90 British Pound

Remarks:
Only available as a kit

## Cirkit Distribution Ltd., Park Lane, Broxbourne, Hertfordshire EN10 7NQ, England

Bezeichnung der Uhr:
**Rewbichron 2**
Empfangbarer Sender:
MSF 60 kHz
Anzeigen für:
Alle von MSF gesendeten Daten

Preis: nicht bekannt

Besonderheit:
Diese Uhr ist nur als Bausatz erhältlich.

Clock's name:
**Rewbichron 2**
Receives time signals from:
MSF 60 kHz
Displays for:
All Data transmitted by MSF

Sales price: not known

Remarks:
The clock only is available as a kit.

## Dyna Electronique, 36 avenue Gambetta, F-75980 Paris Cedex 20, Frankreich/France

Bezeichnung der Uhr:
**Recepteur horaire sur France-Inter G-O**
Empfangbarer Sender:
France Inter 162 kHz
Anzeigen für:
Jahr, Monat, Tag, Wochentag, Stunde, Minute, Sekunde

Preis: mit allen Modulen ca. 15.000 FF

Besonderheiten:
Empfänger, Uhr und Zubehör sind als einzeln erhältliche Module vorhanden und in einem 19-Zoll-Rack einbaubar. Zur Grundausstattung gehört ein Stromversorgungsteil RMS 003 (für 220 V Wechselstrom) oder RMB 003 (für Batteriebetrieb) oder RMA 003 (für 24 V Anschluß), sowie ein Empfängermodul RCH 006 und ein Anzeigemodul AFF 001.

Clock's name:
**Recepteur horaire sur France-Inter G-O**
Receives time signals from:
France Inter 162 kHz
Displays for:
Year, Month, Day, Day of the week, hour, minute, second

Sales price: approx. 15,000 FF (completed with all modules)

Remarks:
Receiver, clock and other options are available as modules, which can be installed into a 19in rack. At least one needs a power supply module RMS 003 (for 220 V AC) or RMB 003 (for battery operation) or RMA 003 (for 24 V DC operation), plus a receiver module RCH 006 and a display module AFF 001.

## European Electronics Systems Ltd., Woodham Mortimer Place, Rectory Lane, Woodham Mortimer, Maldon, Essex CM9 6SW, England

Bezeichnung der Uhr:
**Radio Clock Model 100 und Model 200**
Empfangbarer Sender:
DCF77, MSF, WWV, WWVB oder HBG
Anzeigen für:
Stunden, Minuten, Sekunden
Model 200 zusätzlich: Tag, Monat, Jahr

Preis:

Besonderheit:
Beide Geräte sind als 19-Zoll-Einschubgerät aufgebaut, können aber auch als Tischversion geliefert werden.

Clock's name:
**Radio Clock Model 100 or Model 200**
Receives time signals from:
DCF77, MSF, WWV, WWVB or HBG
Displays for:
Hours, Minutes, Seconds
Model 200 additionally: Day, Month, Year

Sales price:

Remarks:
Both clocks are mounted into a 19in rack, but are also available for a freestanding case.

**Friday Partnership, 14 The Woodland, Wincham, Northwich, Cheshire, CW9 6PL, England**

| | |
|---|---|
| Bezeichnung der Uhr:<br>**FP-788 MSF Rugby Decoder**<br>Empfangbarer Sender:<br>MSF 60 kHz<br>Anzeigen für: Stunden, Minuten,<br>Sekunden, Wochentag, Tag, Monat, Jahr | Clock's name:<br>**FP-788 MSF Rugby Decoder**<br>Receives time signals from:<br>MSF 60 kHz<br>Displays for: Hours, Minutes, Seconds,<br>Day-of-week, Day, Month, Year |
| Preis: ca. 80 Britische Pfund | Sales price: approx. 80 British Pounds |
| Besonderheit:<br>Das Gerät ist nur als Bausatz erhältlich.<br>Es handelt sich um einen reinen Decoder,<br>daher ist zusätzlich ein nicht im Preis<br>enthaltener Funkempfänger für 60 kHz<br>erforderlich. | Remarks:<br>Only available as a kit. The clock does<br>not contain a 60 kHz-receiving<br>source. So an extra RF-receiver is<br>necessary. |

| | |
|---|---|
| **Gebrüder Steiger Uhrenfabrik,<br>Postfach 1432, D-7742 St. Georgen,<br>BRD** | **Gebrüder Steiger Uhrenfabrik,<br>P.O.Box 1432, D-7742 St. Georgen,<br>FRG** |
| Bezeichnung der Uhr:<br>noch offen<br>Empfangbarer Sender:<br>DCF 77<br>Anzeigen für: —— | Clock's name:<br>not yet known<br>Receives time signals from:<br>DCF 77<br>Displays for: —— |
| Preis:<br>noch nicht bekannt | Sales price:<br>not yet knwon |

# Heathkit, Heath Company, Benton Harber, Michigan 49022, USA

Bezeichnung der Uhr:
**Heath GC-1000**
Empfangbarer Sender:
WWV (5, 10 und 15 MHz)
Anzeigen für:
Stunde, Minute, Sekunde, Zehntel-
sekunde, Empfangene Frequenz,
AM-PM (vormittags — nachmittags)

Preis:
ca. 250 US Dollar (als Bausatz)
ca. 425 US Dollar (betriebsbereit und
getestet)

Besonderheit:
Der Empfänger stellt selbsttätig die
am stärksten eintreffende Frequenz ein
und zeigt die eingestellte Frequenz
mittels LED an.
Statt UTC kann die Uhr derart eingestellt
werden, daß sie Lokalzeit anzeigt.

Clock's name:
**Heath GC-1000**
Receives time signals from:
WWV (5, 10 and 15 MHz)
Displays for:
Hour, Minute, Second, Tenth-of-
second, Frequency-in-use,
AM — PM

Sales price:
approx. 250 US Dollars (kit)
approx. 425 US Dollars (assembled
and tested)

Remarks:
LED's show which WWV frequency
is being received and locked by the
receiver automatically.
The clock's time can be converted
from WWV's UTC to any local time.

Hopf Elektronik GmbH,
Postfach 1847,
D-5880 Lüdenscheidt, BRD

Bezeichnung der Uhr:
**Mini-Computer-Funkuhr 4000
und Funkuhr 4200**
Empfangbarer Sender:
DCF 77
Anzeigen für:
Stunden, Minuten, Sekunden,
Wochentag,
zusätzlich beim Model 4200:
Datumangabe (Tag, Monat, Jahr)

Preis:
Typ 4000: ca. 700,– DM;
Typ 4200: ca. 1100,– DM
Beide Uhren sind auch als Bausatz
erhältlich.

Besonderheit:
An beide Uhren ist jeweils eine nicht
im Preis enthaltene externe aktive
Antenne anzuschließen.
Type 4200 ist auch als Schaltuhr
einsetzbar.
Die Fa. Hopf Elektronik GmbH stellt
auch Uhren her, die die codierten
Zeitsignale von France-Inter 162 kHz
auswerten.

Hopf Elektronik GmbH,
P.O.Box 1847,
D-5880 Luedenscheidt, FRG

Clock's name:
**Mini-Computer-Funkuhr 4000
and Funkuhr 4200**
Receives time signals from:
DCF 77
Displays for:
Hours, minutes, seconds,
day of the week,
the clock type 4200 additional:
Date (day, month, year)

Sales price:
Type 4000: approx. 700,– DM;
Type 4200: approx. 1100 DM.
Both clocks also are available
as kits.

Remarks:
Both clocks need an external active
antenna, which is not included in the
sales price above.
Type 4200 also can be used as a
switching clock.
Hopf Elektronik GmbH also offers
clocks using the coded time signals
of France Inter 162 kHz.

Junghans Uhren GmbH,
Postfach 100/120,
D-7230 Schramberg, BRD

Junghans Uhren GmbH,
P.O.Box 100/120,
D-7230 Schramberg, FRG

Bezeichnung der Uhr:
**Junghans-Funkuhr (1),**
**Avantgarde (2)**
Empfangbarer Sender:
DCF 77
Anzeigen für:
Stunden, Minuten, Sekunden
(analog auf zwei getrennten Ziffer-
blättern)

Preis:
nicht bekannt (1),
ca. 980,– DM (2)

Besonderheit:
Die Junghans-Funkuhr ist eine Tisch-
uhr, das Modell Avantgarde eine Wand-
uhr. Beide Uhren arbeiten als reine
Quarzuhren. Zu jeder vollen Stunde
werden die DCF 77-Signale empfangen,
um ggf. das Quarzwerk nachzustellen.

Clock's name:
**Junghans-Funkuhr (1),**
**Avantgarde (2)**
Receives time signals from:
DCF 77
Displays for:
Hours, minutes, seconds
(analog on two separate scales)

Sales price:
not known (1),
approx. 980,– DM (2)

Remarks:
The Junghans-Funkuhr is a table
model, Avantgarde is a wall-clock.
Both clocks work as quartz-
crystal clocks; on the full hour
DCF 77-signals are received for
adjustment purposes.

## Kinemetrics/Truetime, 3243 Santa Rosa Ave., Santa Rosa, CA 95407, USA

Bezeichnung der Uhr:
**60-DC** für WWVB-Empfang
(+ A-60FS Antenne)
**LF-DC** für MSF und DCF77-Empfang
(+ A-LFS Antenne)
Empfangbarer Sender:
siehe oben
Anzeigen für:
Stunde, Minute, Sekunde
sind an der Uhr ablesbar.
Weitere Daten können einem separaten
Ausgang entnommen und zur Anzeige
an externen Geräten gebracht werden.

Preis: wurde vom Hersteller nicht genannt.

Besonderheit:
Die Uhr ist als 19-Zoll-Tischgerät
aufgebaut.
Kinemetrics/Truetime stellt außerdem
Uhren für den Empfang der GOES-
und GPS-Satelliten her.

Clock's name:
**60-DC** for WWVB-Reception
(plus A-60FS Antenna)
**LF-DC** for MSF- and DCF77-
reception (plus A-LFS-Antenna)
Receives time signals from:
see above
Displays for:
Hours, minutes, seconds are shown
at the clock's display. Further data
offered by the time signal station
received are offered at a separate
output for connecting extern
devices.

Sales price: not published by the
manufacturer

Remarks:
The clock is installed in a 19in rack
or bench top.
Kinemetrics/Truetime also produces
clocks which use the signal of the
GOES- and GPS-satellites.

## Kundo Quartz, Kieninger & Obergfell, Postfach/P.O.Box 81, D-7742 St. Georgen, BRD/FRG

Bezeichnung der Uhr:
**Space timer**
Empfangbarer Sender:
DCF 77
Anzeigen für:
Stunden, Minuten, Sekunden
Datum (Tag und Monat) (digital)

Preis: ca. 500,– DM

Besonderheit:
Die Uhr arbeitet mit ihrer Quarzzeitbasis als reine Quarzuhr. Lediglich
nachts um 00.00, 02.00, 03.00 und
04.00 Uhr (Einlesezeiten) empfängt
die Uhr die DCF 77-Signale, um
eventuelle Abweichungen zu korrigieren.

Clock's name:
**Space timer**
Receives time signals from:
DCF 77
Displays for:
Hours, minutes, seconds (analog)
Date (Day and Month) (digital)

Sales price: approx. 500,– DM

Remarks:
The clock works on a quartz-crystal
time basis. At 00.00, 02.00, 03.00
and 04.00 UTC, the clock is receiving
the DCF 77-signals for adjustment
purposes.

## Precision Standard Time Inc., 2585 Scott Blvd., Santa Clara, CA 95050, USA

Bezeichnung der Uhr:
**OEM-10**
Empfangbarer Sender
WWV und WWVH
Anzeigen für:
alle von WWV und WWVH übermittelten Daten
Preis:
270,– bis 450,– US Dollar
(je nach Abnahmemenge)

Besonderheit:
Der Preis beinhaltet nur den in der Abbildung dargestellten Empfänger. Zusätzlich wird noch ein nicht im Preis enthaltenes Display für die Zeitansage benötigt.
Der Empfänger scannt alle WWV/WWVH-Frequenzen ab und nutzt das jeweils stärkste Signal zur Umsetzung für eine externe Digitalanzeige.

Clock's name:
**OEM-10**
Receives time signals from:
WWV and WWVH
Displays for:
all dates offered by WWV and WWVH

Sales price:
270.00 to 450.00 US Dollar price range, depending on quantities purchased.

Remarks:
The price only includes the receiver and not an extra needed extern digital display.
The OEM-10 scans all five WWV frequencies, locks on to one with the best data integrity, converts the signal into a digital output and continues to receive time updates.

## Radiocode Clocks Ltd., Unit 19, Parkengue, Kernick Road Industrial Estate, Penryn, Cornwall TR10 9EP, UK

Bezeichnung der Uhr:
**Radiocode Clock, Model RCC 8000**
Empfangbarer Sender:
Entweder MSF 60 kHz
oder DCF77 77,5 kHz
oder HGB 75 kHz
oder WWVB 60 kHz
Anzeigen für:
alle von dem jeweiligen Sender angebotenen Daten
Preis:
nicht bekannt
Besonderheit:
Die Uhr ist für den Einbau in einem 19-Zoll-Einschub vorgesehen. Sie arbeitet bei Senderausfall mit ihrer Quarzzeitbasis selbständig weiter, und mit dem Standby Supply auch noch bei Stromausfall.

Clock's name:
**Radiocode Clock, Model RCC 8000**
Receives time signals from:
Either MSF 60 kHz
or DCF77 77,5 kHz
or HGB 75 kHz
or WWVB 60 kHz
Displays for:
All data offered by the received time signal radio station
Sales price:
not known
Remarks:
The clock is prepared for a 19in rack mounting. In a case of a transmitter failure, the clock continues working on a built-in quartz-crystal time basis. Together with an additional standby supply the clock even continues in the case of a mains failure.

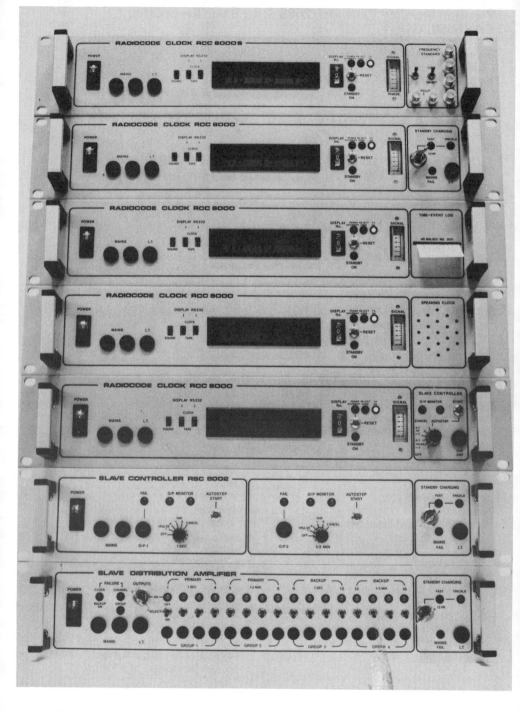

**telematique SA, Zirst-chemin des prés, F-38 240 Meylan, France/ Frankreich**

Bezeichnung der Uhr:
**RTD 101**
Empfangbarer Sender:
France-Inter (162 kHz)
Anzeigen für:
Stunden, Minuten, Sekunden, Jahr,
Monat, Tag.
Die Anzeige ist wahlweise schaltbar
für die Anzeige von S, M und S oder
für J, M und T.

Preis:
nicht bekannt

Besonderheit:
Die Uhr ist in einem 19-Zoll-Einschub
eingebaut

Clock's name:
**RTD 101**
Receives time signals from:
France-Inter (162 kHz)
Displays for:
Hours, minutes, seconds, year,
month, day —
switchable (either H, M and S or Y,
M and D can be shown on the
display)

Sales price:
not knwon

Remarks:
The clock is built into a 19 inch rack

## Trak Microwave Corporation, 4726 Eisenhower Boulevard, Tampa, Florida 33614, USA

Bezeichnung der Uhr:
**Model 8600**
Empfangbarer Sender:
GOES Zeitzeichensatellit
Anzeigen für:
UTC oder Lokalzeit;
Differenz zwischen UTC und Lokalzeit;
eigene geographische Koordinaten;
geogr. Koordinaten des empfangenen
Satelliten; Entfernung zum Satelliten;
Grad der angezeigten Zeitgenauigkeit

Preis: − ? −

Besonderheit:
Das Gerät ist in einem 19-Zoll-Einschub
eingebaut.
Externe Anschlußmöglichkeit von
Geräten zur Darstellung von:
IRIG B-code
BCD-code
IEEE-488 time
RS-232 time.
Das Gerät berechnet selbsttätig die
Signallaufzeit vom Satelliten zum
Empfänger anhand der eigenen ein-
gegebenen Koordinaten und korri-
giert anhand der berechneten Laufzeit
die angezeigte Zeit.

Clock's name:
**Model 8600**
Receives time signals from:
GOES Time-Signals Satellite
Displays for:
UTC or local time,
Hours offset between UTC and
local time; Local longitude
preset value; Local latitude preset
value; Satellite's longitude and
latitude; Satellite's radious;
Expected accuracy

Sales price: − ? −

Remarks:
Clock is built into a 19in rack.
Outputs provided include:
IRIG-B,
BCD-code,
IEEE-488 time,
RS-232 time.
The clock is making a path cor-
rection based on received data.

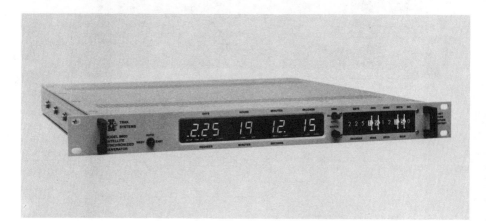

## Radio Shack, 1700 One Tandy Center, Forth Worth, Texas 76102, USA

Bezeichnung der Uhr:
  **Realistic Weatheradio/Timekube**
Empfangbarer Sender:
  WWV Fort Collins (5, 10, 15 MHz)
Anzeigen für: —

Preis: 39,95 US Dollar

Besonderheiten:
  Es handelt sich hierbei um einen
  Empfänger, der wahlweise (in den USA
  sendende) Wetterstationen oder die
  Zeitzeichenstation WWV auf 5, 10 oder
  15 MHz empfängt und akustisch hör-
  bar macht. Anhand der Zeitansagen ist
  die im Empfänger eingebaute Analoguhr
  ein- bzw. nachzustellen.

Clock's name:
  **Realistic Weatheradio/Timekube**
Receives time signals from:
  WWV Fort Collins (5, 10, 15 MHz)
Displays for: —

Sales price: 39.95 US Dollar

Remarks:
  Receives weather radio stations
  (inside the USA) or the time signal
  radio station WWV on 5, 10 or
  15 MHz. The time signals can be
  heard with the receiver's loud-
  speaker and can be used to adjust or
  readjust the built-in analog clock.

# Aktieselskabet Erling B. Ibsen, Metalbuen 28, DK-2750 Ballerup, Dänemark/Denmark

Bezeichnung der Uhr:
Empfangbarer Sender:
**NCX10-9 TSI** für HBG-Empfang
**RBX 10-9 TSI** für MSF-Empfang
**MFX 10-9 TSI** für DCF77-Empfang

Clock's name:
Receives time signals from:
**NCX 10-9 TSI** for HBG-75-reception
**RBX 10-9 TSI** for MSF-60-reception
**MFX 10-9 TSI** for DCF77-reception

Anzeigen für: —

Displays for: —

Preis:
ca. 14.000 Dänische Kronen

Sales price:
approx. 14.000 Danish Crowns

Besonderheit:
Es handelt sich nicht um eine Uhr, sondern jeweils um einen für HGB-, MSF- oder DCF-Empfang ausgelegten Längswellenempfänger. Der Empfänger ermöglicht die akustische Wiedergabe der Zeitsignale und setzt sie außerdem in 0,1 Hz, 1 Hz, 10 Hz, 100 Hz, 1 kHz, 10 kHz, 100 kHz, 1 MHz and 10 MHz-Signale.

Remarks:
Does not mark as a clock but as a VLF-receiver either for HBG-, MSF- or DCF77-signals. The time signals are available accustically. Furthermore the time signals are converted to 0.1 Hz-, 1 Hz-, 10 Hz-, 100 Hz-, 1 kHz-, 10 kHz-, 100 kHz-, 1 MHz- and 10 MHz-signals.

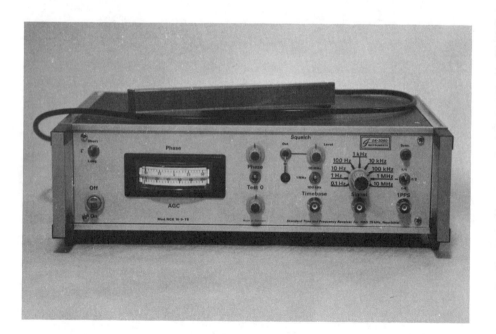

## Weitere Funkuhrenhersteller:

## Further manufacturers
## of remote controlled clocks:

Name und Adresse:
Name and address:

Empfangbare Zeitzeichenstation:
Received station:

ZPA Pragotron, Podebradská 22,
CSSR-180 39 Prague 9                          OMA

Teknis Electronics
Teknis House, Meadrow,
Godalming, Surrey, England                    MSF

Despro Electronic Ltd.
Orgreave Crescent,
Dore House Industrial Estate,
Handworth, Sheffield S13 9 NQ,
England                                       MSF

RBDK (Electric) Ltd., Beechwood,
Holly Bank Road, Wook Heath,
Woking, Surrey GU22 OJW, England              MSF

Caringella Electronics Inc.,
P.O.Box 727
Upland, CA 91786, USA                         WWVB

Arbiter Systems Inc.
P.O.Box 996
Goleta, CA 93116, USA                         GOES Satellites

# 10. Abbreviations

# 10. Abkürzungen

| | | |
|---|---|---|
| BCD | Binary Coded Decimal | Binärkodierung |
| BIH | Bureau International de l'Heure | Internationales Zeitbüro |
| BST | British Summer Time | Britische Sommerzeit |
| CCIR | International Radio Consultative Committee | |
| CEST/MESZ | Central European Summer Time | Mitteleuropäische Sommerzeit |
| CET/MEZ | Central European Time | Mitteleuropäische Zeit |
| CW | Continuous Wave | Im Morsecode übertragene Sendung |
| DUT | See under "Time Scales" | Siehe unter „Zeitskalen" |
| DUT1 | See under "Time Scales" | Siehe unter „Zeitskalen" |
| FSK | Frequency Shift Keying | Steuerung durch Frequenzänderung |
| G.C./G.K. | Geographical Coordinates | Geographische Koordinaten |
| GMT | Greenwich Mean Time | Normalzeit des Nullten Längengrads |
| GOES | Geostationary Operational Environmental Satellite | |
| GPS | Global Positioning System | |
| h | hour(s) | Stunde(n) |
| LORAN | Long Range Aid to Navigation | Langstreckennavigationssystem |
| m | minute(s) | Minute(n) |
| ms | millisecond(s) | Millisekunde(n) |
| OCXO | Oven controlled quartz-crystal oscillator | Thermostatkontrollierter Quarzoszillator |
| Rp | Return postage | Rückporto |
| s | second(s) | Sekunde(n) |
| TAI | Temps Atomique Internationale | Internationale Atomzeit |
| TC | Time Code | Zeitcode |
| TCXO | Temperature controlled quartz-crystal oscillator | Temperaturkompensierter Quarzoszillator |
| UT | Universal Time | Universalzeit |
| UTC | Universal Time Coordinated | Koordinierte Universalzeit |
| V | Verification | Bestätigung |
| VCXO | Voltage controlled quartz-crystal oscillator | Spannungsstabilisierter Quarzoszillator |
| VLF | very low frequency | sehr niedrige Frequenz |
| XO | Quartz-crystal oscillator | Quarzoszillator |